The Inner Workings of the Oil and Gas Business

Terry W. Piesker

PAGE PUBLISHING, INC.
New York, NY

First originally published by Page Publishing, Inc. 2014

ISBN 978-1-63417-224-0 (pbk)
ISBN 978-1-63417-225-7 (digital)

Printed in the United States of America

CONTENTS

FOREWORD

This book is a quick overview of the oil and gas business in the simplest of terms. It is designed for the oil investor, anyone interested in how the oil field really works, and the engineer planning on getting into the business.

I have two stepsons who are in the business. This is why I decided that someone needed to write a book about the oil business. My youngest son is in the process of coming back to Kansas to take over his father's independent oil company. He has no idea what the business entails. He will be learning from the grassroots up. They were in town during the New Year's holiday, and his wife asked me if there was a book he could get that would teach him about the oil patch. I laughed and said, "The only way to learn this business is by experience." What I had said made me think. There are basics that you need to know. This is what got me started.

The oil patch has its own language. In this book, you will find that I have gone through every aspect of the business, from how a prospect is generated, right down to the maintenance of the well itself. This book encompasses a lot of information. I have tried to write it in layman's terms so it can be easily understood.

I have been in this business for over forty years. I have a bachelor of science degree in education from Emporia State University,

Emporia, Kansas, with majors in math and social science. Upon my graduation in 1974, I went to work for Cities Service Oil Company as an engineering technician. In May 1975, I was promoted to assistant production foreman in El Dorado, Kansas. After two years, I took a job as Rocky Mountain district engineer for Petroleum Incorporated in Kimball, Nebraska. A year later I moved back to Russell, Kansas, as engineer / assistant production foreman for Frontier Oil Company. In 1989 the company was sold to AFG Energy Inc., and at that time, I became in charge of everything. The company was sold again in 1999 to Tengasco Inc. In late 1999, I became president of Tengasco Inc. and moved back to Knoxville, Tennessee. In September 2000, I moved back to Hays, Kansas, as an independent consultant. January 1, 2002, I went to work for Dreiling Oil Inc. I worked at Dreiling Oil Inc., putting deals together and taking care of their production. I am now an independent consultant.

I have completed or worked over well over two thousand oil and gas wells in Wyoming, Tennessee, and Kansas. I have set up hundreds of leases and new wells. I have overseen operations of several hundred wells and leases. I have been involved in operations, drilling, and promotions of new development as well as finding investors. Most of my experience has been on the Central Kansas Uplift in Kansas. This is one of the most diversified and difficult areas in the world. I have had some excellent tutors over the years. I would like to take time to acknowledge some of these people, most of all, my stepfather, Frank Robinson, who got me interested in the business during the summers of my college years, working for Cities Service Oil Company; Mr. Richard Parker, Frontier Oil Company; Mr. George Angle, Frontier Oil Company; Mr. Charles Forrester, Cities Service Oil Company; and all of the people who have worked under me or for me over the years. I learn something new in this business almost every day. If you don't, you are not paying attention.

The only way to truly learn this business is by being on location and getting firsthand experience. I've been around many a book-trained engineer. Most of them have very little field experience. This book would be extremely beneficial to them.

Hopefully, this book will fill a real void in our industry. I hope you enjoy it.

1

PROSPECT GENERATION

When I started in this business, prospect generation was done almost solely by a geologist. A geologist would look at an area that he liked, say four or five sections. He would then draw out a map with all the previous wells drilled, dry holes and producers. All large companies and some geologists had card files by Section, Township, and Range of every well drilled. These card files have the formation tops on most all the zones in the area. The geologist would spot the locations on a map, make copies of the maps, and plot subsea (minus) elevations for each horizon of interest. As an example, he would make a subsea map for the tops of the Topeka, the Heebner (which is not a producing zone but it is a great marker, shale), The Lansing-Kansas City, and the Arbuckle, depending where the well is located or some other producing zone below the Lansing-Kansas City. He would then contour the maps. Contouring is a lot like drawing by the dots, except you are drawing by using the subsea footages. Diagram A is an example of contouring. He is trying to get a picture of what the terrain looks like a few thousand feet below the surface. From this map, he would be trying to find locations that would be considerably higher than the dry holes and at least flat or higher than the producers. This is a very subjective map, which I will call the hope-and-pray method of picking a location. In other words, the prospective location was nothing more than one person's semieducated guess.

In the late 1990s, 3-D imaging came into the picture. It took several years for this to become perfected. 3-D imaging is a seismic interpretation of what each horizon looks like, using sound waves and time to determine depths. Lines and recorders are laid across the acreage in specific patterns. Once these lines are laid out, a vibrator (large truck with vibrator pad) goes between these lines on a designated route and stomps every so often. As the truck goes along, it stops in certain spots and vibrates the ground. These sounds go down and bounce off the various rock formations below and come back up to the surface and are picked up by the recording devices placed on the surface and hooked to a recording truck. These sound waves are then recorded. A record of these are kept and interpreted. Once this is done, a geophysicist can take this interpretation and make maps of the processed area. If everything comes out correctly, they can be quite accurate. There are things that can bother this type of work. Nature itself can be a problem, such as wind. The salt section, if the area has one, can be a real problem if it is eroded. The old method of contouring probably had a fifty-fifty chance in a proven area and about a 25% chance in a wildcat area. With 3-D imaging, this is about 75% to 80% in proven areas and about 50% in wildcat areas. Thus, as an investor, your chances are much better than twenty-five years ago.

With the 3-D imaging, the geologist can now pick up a much larger area, say 10 miles. He maps this out and does his contouring, just like before. After doing this, he may decide that there is some of this with potential and some that has no potential. Instead of looking for one spot location, he now looks for an area, hopefully with more than one location. He may decide that only 4 or 5 miles of this contouring has potential. He then checks to make sure all the acreage he wants is open at the courthouse. Open, in this instance, means unleased. From here he goes out and tries to lease the acreage, either on his own or with the help of a landman. A landman is a professional who does this for a job. He does this for several companies. Usually a geologist either works for a company or he is on his own, what we call an independent. Also, oftentimes larger companies will buy prospects from an independent geologist. The company or geologist leases the land in their name. This acreage is leased and recorded at the courthouse of the county in which the acreage lays. These leases can be any duration, but they are usually two to five years, depending on how long you can get it leased from the mineral owner. Keep in mind you are leasing the acreage from the mineral owner, not necessarily the landowner. In other words, the landowner may or may not own the minerals under the ground. When land is sold, it can be sold with or without the minerals. Thus, depending on the acreage you are leasing, the landowner and the mineral owner may or may not be the same person. In addition, you may be dealing with several mineral owners on the same acreage. Over the years, mineral owners have passed away, and they have divided the minerals up between their heirs. I have leased acreage with as many as twenty-four different mineral owners on one plot of acreage. Each one of these mineral owners needs to sign the lease and receive their share of the lease money. Also, minerals can be sold either all or part of their interest. All of this will be recorded at the county courthouse in which the acreage is located. That's how you find out the mineral owners to each lease you are planning on picking up. This can be a tedious job.

Once the land is leased, the company or geologist seeks to find investors. These are people who want to take the chance that a well or wells will be found. I call these people the gamblers. When I do this, I usually go around with what we call an authority for expenditure (AFE), which you will find in diagram B. This includes the cost of the acreage, my finder's fee for the project, the cost of the 3-D for the project area, and an estimated cost to drill the first well on the project. This helps to give the investor a good idea of what the project will cost so he can make a rational decision on whether or not he is interested in the project. He should also want to know what the net revenue interest (NRI) of the project will be. This will be the same for all wells on the project.

Let me explain NRI. In Kansas an ordinary lease is usually $10 to $25 per acre depending on where the acreage is located. The lease agreement states that the mineral owner gets 1/8 (12.5%) of everything produced from any well drilled on their acreage. This is called the royalty interest (RI). This may vary in Texas and Oklahoma, up to 25%. Everything in this book will deal with a straight 1/8 royalty. The landowner pays no expenses for this 1/8 royalty. This is what we call a standard lease, which is attached as exhibit C. This lease is for a specific term, say three years. What this means is that you have a lease on this particular acreage for a term of three years. You have three years to sell this project, 3-D the acreage, and generate the prospects to be drilled. In other words, you have three years to drill your well or wells. Once you have a producing well on any part of the lease, you have this acreage for the duration of the well without any fees. If you drill a dry hole, this does not hold the acreage. It must be a producing well. If after drilling a dry hole you are still interested in this lease, you have to drill another well that must be a producer or negotiate an extension on the original lease before it runs out.

This project will consist of many different leases. More than likely, these 4 or 5 sections will not be all one lease. Every lease is independent. In other words, you have to drill a producing well on each separate lease to hold the acreage. There may be a lot of different landowners in these 4 or 5 sections. Get your lease agreements as large as possible so that one well will hold as much acreage as possible.

Here is how you figure out the NRI for the project. You start out with 100% and subtract the 12.5% royalty interest. The geologist usually takes what we call an overriding royalty interest (ORRI) for putting the project together. On my projects I try to keep the NRI at 82.5%. Thus, I get a 5% ORRI. This interest does not pay any expenses either. The only way I make any money on this project is when we get a producing well. This is just like a royalty interest.

Some operators, in addition to an ORRI, get a free ride to the bottom of the hole. This means they pay no expenses until the decision is made whether or not to set pipe or plug the well. If the well is plugged, they have no expenses. If the pipe is set, they pay their percentage of the working interest expenses from this point on including the price of the pipe.

Working interest owners pay 100% of the expenses on the lease. Depending on what the final NRI is, that is the percentage of income the working interest owners will receive for revenue from the lease.

It used to be that WIs were sold in 1/16 (6.25%), 1/8 (12.5%), 1/32 (3.125%), and 1/64 (1.5625%). Personally, I believe this was done simply to complicate the system—in other words, to make it tougher for the investor to really understand. Keep in mind, some of the people in this business, as in any other business, might be a little shady. These are the people that give this business a bad name. I call these people promoters. Keep in mind that you always want to get in business with people who have a good reputation and are honest. Check them out before you invest with anyone in this business. Do your homework. Large oil companies, which we call majors, are usually pretty sound. You can invest in these by buying stock. Many of the smaller oil companies listed on the over-the-counter exchange can be rather scary. A lot of these companies are run by accountants who know nothing about the oil and gas business. They have no idea how a real oil company should operate. They're great with money and numbers, but that's not what the oil business really entails. Sure, it takes money to get into this business, but it also takes oil know-how to make money. Lots of these small companies will be out of business in five to ten years. If the oil industry has a downturn over the next twenty years, they'll never make it. You want to invest in a company that can stand the test of time. Don't be conned by these simple ads to own your own oil well. You'd have to be an idiot to get sucked into one of these companies. Check out the people you are investing with. If it sounds too easy or good, it probably is.

Now let me explain how this all works in a little more detail. I sell my WI divisions out in 5%, 10%, 20%, and so on. It makes things much easier to understand. The investor is offered a part of the project. He can take whatever interest he would like based on how much risk he wants to take. Let's say an investor takes 20% of a project. This is a 20% WI. From above, the NRI for WI owners is 82.5%. Thus, the WI owner would pay 20% of 100% of the expenses and receive 20% of

82.5% of the revenue from the sale of oil or gas from this project. Let me break this down below.

> 100% expenses paid by working interest owners (Whatever the WI percentage, he pays that percentage of all expenses.)
>
> Let's say the monthly expenses are $2,000. The WI owner has a 20% WI.
>
> Thus he would pay $400 of the $2,000 bill.

	revenue interest	100%
–	royalty interest	12.5%
		87.5%
–	ORRI	5.0%
	NRI	82.5%

total expenses × 20% WI = WI owners bill
total revenues × 82.5% × 20% WI = 16.5% NRI

Now all you have to do is sell out the 100% WI in the project. Once you have this done, you need to find a geophysicist, and it's on to the shooting of the acreage.

I pretty well explained how the 3-D operates earlier in this section. Once the geophysicist has had a chance to map the area with the processed 3-D, the geologist or company man will meet with the geophysicist and go over the project. He will have had time to come up with locations. Usually he will have them in some sort of order, call it A, B, and C locations. The A locations are the ones that he feels more confident with. They would be the first ones to try. The B locations are the locations that are a little more risky. Then the C locations are real risky. He will have maps of the tops that are the easiest to pick out, such as the Anhydrite, Topeka, Heebner, Base of the L-KC, and Basement. To me the most important thing are the cross sections. Attached, you will find a cross section, exhibit D. These are the wave links of the 3-D going from well to well. These are usually through producing wells, dry holes, and the possible spot locations of wells to be drilled. I spend a tremendous amount of time looking at these. They show you the highs and lows of the project along with the proposed locations that you might want to drill. The first thing I do when I get the cross sections is put the subsea tops of all the wells on each of the cross sections to see if everything appears to fit with what we know. Sometimes the geophysicist does not have time to do this. I make the time because I think it is very important. One of the hardest markers to find is the Arbuckle. Sometimes it cannot be distinguished. In other words, there is no real reflector to indicate the top of the Arbuckle. In a case like this, the best reflector to look at is below the Basement top. You are looking for hills. Usually these show up quite well below the Basement top. They may not always be right, but they are a good indicator. Once again, you are looking for something that looks higher than other wells. Often this can be found quite easily as you move across the cross section. They will tend to look like little hills. You pick out some marker close to the productive horizon you are looking at and move along that line. Hopefully it will just stick out at you. Refer back to exhibit D, a cross section, to see what I mean. Once you have made the decision on the location you will try to drill first, you need to have an attorney do a title search to make sure you have a legal lease agreement with the correct mineral owners. This is very important. You do not want to drill a well unless you have a legal lease on the ground. You may end up drilling a well that someone else may end up owning if you don't do your homework. Many times, as mentioned earlier, the landowners do not own the minerals on the acreage. You need to make sure your attorney knows what he is doing. Once you know you have the lease, you can go on to the next step.

You call the survey crew into action. You call them and give them the exact spot location of the well to be drilled. It would look something like this:

Young 1
990' from the east line (FEL) and 330' from the
north line (FNL)
Section 23- Township 18S-, Range 13W
Ellis County, Kansas

The survey crew will go out and put a stake at this exact location. They will also give you the ground level elevation that you will need. Elevation is measured from sea level. From here, you contract a drilling contractor to drill the well along with other various contractors you will need to use during the drilling of the well. You will need a mud man, a pipe supply company for your surface pipe and long sting, a cement company to cement pipe in place, a logging company, and a drill stem test company. By the time you get through the next chapter, you will know what each of these companies does.

If you are working for a licensed oil company, you are ready to file your intent to drill with the state corporation commission. If you are planning on starting your own company, you will have to make application with the state for an operator's license. Once you have received your license, you can file the intent to drill. Attached you will find the intent to drill form for the state of Kansas, exhibit E. When it has been approved, the state will send you back an API number for the well. This API number will stay with the well forever. All states will have this in some similar form. Once all this has been completed, you are ready to drill your first well.

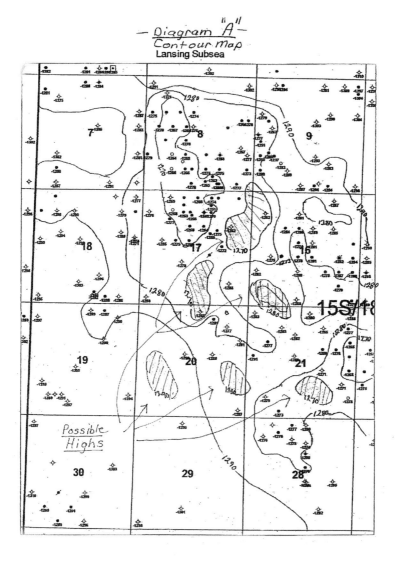

Diagram "A"
Contour map
Lansing Subsea

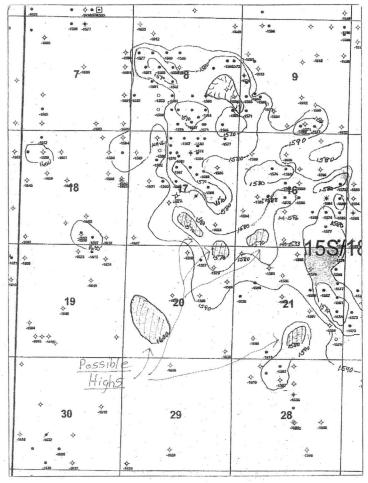

Diagram "A"
Contour Map
Arbuckle Subsea

Diagram "B"

COST ANALYSIS AND PROSPECT DATA
NORTHEAST TOULON 3D SEISMIC PROJECT
ELLIS COUNTY, KANSAS

I. **Lease data:**
    Oil and Gas lease map attached.

Township 13S and 14S- Range 17W   Ellis County, Kansas

Section 33-	NE/4	160 Acres
	E/2 of W/2	160 Acres
	W/2 of W/2	150 Acres
Section 3-	E/2 of NE/4	80 Acres
	W/2 of NE/4 and NW/4	240 Acres
Section 4-	NE/4	160 Acres
	NE/4, SE/4, and SW/4 of NW/4	120 Acres
	NW/4. NE/4, and SE/4 of the SW/4	110 Acres
	SW/4 of SW/4	40 Acres
Section 5-	S/2 of NE/4	80 Acres
	SE/4	160 Acres
Section 8-	N/2 of NW/4	80 Acres
	NW/4 of NE/4	40
Section 9-	NW/4	160 Acres
	NE/4	150 Acres

TOTAL ACRES-   1890 Acres

1890 Acres Total- 200 Acres Farmed Out and 1690
Acres Leased Acreage- 1690 Acres X $15.00/Acre $25,350.00

All Leases will be delivered at 82.5% Net Revenue Interest except the following:

NE/4, SE/4 and SW/4 of the NW/4 of Section 5-14S-17W, Ellis County, which will be delivered at a Net Revenue Interest of 82.0313%.

There are two Farmouts in this package. They are as follows:

17

N/2 of the NW/4 of Section 8-14S-17W (80 Acres) The NRI on this
will be 82.5%. There will be no lease cost for this acreage. The
present Company will retain a 5% ORRI with a conversion right after
12,000 Barrels of oil have been produced from the first well on the
lease. At That time they have the choice of converting their ORRI to a
12.5% Working Interest.

The second Farmout is on the NE/4, SE/4, and the SW/4 of the NW/4
of Section 4- 14S-17W (120 Acres). The ORRI on this lease is
presently 5.4687%. To Farmout this acreage we had to give the present
company a 25% Working Interest Option after the first well on the
lease has produced 12,000 Barrel of oil. If the option is taken,
all Working Interests will be cut proportionally. No lease money will
be paid for this lease.

II.   **Geological and Prospect Origination Fee:** $5,000

III   **Geophysical Expenses:**
        Cost to Acquire 3.06 Miles of 3D Seismic Data: $99,144
                        20% Promote = $118.973
        (1960 Acres will be shot- the 10 acre sights
        on all leases and the NW/4 of NW/4 of
        Section 4-14S-17W will be shot.)

IV.   **Total Cost Before Drilling to Investor Group:** $149,323
        100% of the Lease Costs, Geological and
        Geophysical expenses required for Drill Site
        Selection.

                        Cost of Working Interest Share:

Investor Interest	Cost to Investor
100%	$149,323
50%	$ 74,662
37.5%	$ 55,996
25%	$ 37,331
12.5%	$ 18,666
10%	$ 14,932
5%	$ 7,466

V. **Estimated Cost Per Well (see copy of AFE for details):**

Drilling-		$67,317
Completion and Equipment-		$73,870
Total per Well Estimated Cost-		$141,187

INTEREST	BEFORE DRILLING	DRILLING	COMP. @ EQUIP	TOTAL
100%	$149,323	$67,317	$73,870	$290,510
50%	$ 74,662	$33,659	$36,935	$145,256
37.5%	$ 55,996	$25,244	$27,701	$108,941
25%	$ 37,331	$16,829	$18,468	$ 72,628
12.5%	$ 18,666	$ 8,415	$ 9,234	$ 36,315
10%	$ 14,932	$ 6,732	$ 7,387	$ 29,051
5%	$ 7,466	$ 3,366	$ 3,694	$ 14,526

I (We) wish to participate for a _____ % Working Interest in the above prospect along with all costs as outlined above.

Company or Individual Name: _____

Signature of Individual Responsible: _____

Date: _____

19

Authorization for Expenditure
Drilling and Completion

INTANGIBLE WELL COSTS

		DRY HOLE	PRODUCING WELL
1.	Lease Cost (Title Expense)	$ 500.00	
2.	Leveling Location and Dig Pits-	$ 500.00	
3.	Running Elevation and Staking	$ 250.00	
4.	Hauling and Welding Surface Pipe	$ 500.00	
5.	Cement/Cement Equipment/Cement Services		
	Surface $1,842 Prod.$9,500	$ 4,042.00	$7,300.00
	Plug $2,200		
6.	Drilling Costs		
	3650' @ $9.00 per foot	$ 32,850.00	
	60 hours Day Work at $183.33/hr.	$ 10.999.80	
7.	Drill Stem Tests- 3 @ $950 each	$ 2,850.00	
8.	Mud	$ 3,500.00	
9.	Water	$ 1,500.00	
	Water Hauling	$ 0	
10.	Electric Logs	$ 3.200.00	
11.	Well Site Geologist-4 Days @ $350/Day	$ 1,400.00	
12.	Backfilling Pits and Leveling	$ 1,000.00	
13.	Crop and Surface Damages	$ 500.00	
14.	Trucking	$	$ 2,000.00
15.	Supervision	$ 1,000.00	$ 1,500.00
16.	Completion Unit- 3 Days @ $1,600/Day		$ 4,800.00
17.	Perforating and Cement Bond Log		$ 1,500.00
18.	Treating		$ 2,000.00
19.	Plug and Packer Rental		$ 1,800.00
20.	Casing Crew		$ 2,000.00
21.	Other (Backhoe, Water Hauling, Road, etc.)	$ 1,000.00	$ 1,000.00

TOTAL INTANGIBLES $ 65,591.80   **$23.900.00**

TANGIBLE WELL COSTS

1.	Casing	225' - 8 5/8" Casing @ $6.90/Ft.	$1,725.00	
		3650' - 5 ½" Casing @ ($ 3.90/Ft)		$14,235.00

2.	Tubing		
	3650 Feet of 2 7/8" @ $2.90	$0.00	$10,585.00
3.	Rods		
	3650 Feet of ¾" @ $1.00	$0.00	$3,650.00
4.	PVC Flowline		
	1200 Feet of 3" @ $1.25	$0.00	$1,500.00
5.	Pumping Unit and Engine	$0.00	$7,000.00
6.	Tank Battery	$0.00	$10,000.00
7.	Well Head Connections	$0.00	$2,000.00
8.	Miscellaneous	$0.00	$1,000.00

TOTAL TANGIBLES	**$1,725.00**	**$49,970.00**

TOTAL BOTTOM HOLE COST   **$67,316.80**

PROMOTE 1.2 (initial well only)
LEASEHOLD
GEOLOGICAL FEE

TOTAL COST	**$67,316.80**	**$73,870.00**
	Dry Hole	Additional Cost
		Of Producer

GRAND TOTAL	**$67,316.80**	**$141,186.80**

This is only an estimate. Cost may increase or decrease at the time of drilling. This will give you some idea of what the actual costs will be if a prospect is developed.

Exhibit "C".
(Standard Oil & Gas Lease)

FORM 88 — (PRODUCER'S SPECIAL) (PAID-UP)

63U (Rev. 1995)

OIL AND GAS LEASE

Reorder No.
09-115

Kansas Blue Print

AGREEMENT, Made and entered into the _____ day of _____

by and between _____

whose mailing address is _____ hereinafter called Lessor (whether one or more),

and _____ hereinafter called Lessee:

Lessor, in consideration of _____ Dollars ($ _____) in hand paid, receipt of which is here acknowledged and of the royalties herein provided and of the agreements of the lessee herein contained, hereby grants, leases and lets exclusively unto lessee for the purpose of investigating, exploring by geophysical and other means, prospecting drilling, mining and operating for and producing oil, liquid hydrocarbons, all gases, and their respective constituent products, injecting gas, water, other fluids, and air into subsurface strata, laying pipe lines, storing oil, building tanks, power stations, telephone lines, and other structures and things thereon to produce, save, take care of, treat, manufacture, process, store and transport said oil, liquid hydrocarbons, gases and their respective constituent products and other products manufactured therefrom, and housing and otherwise caring for its employees, the following described land, together with any reversionary rights and after-acquired interest, therein situated in County of _____ State of _____ described as follows to-wit:

In Section _____ Township _____ Range _____ and containing _____ acres, more or less, and all accretions thereto.

Subject to the provisions herein contained, this lease shall remain in force for a term of _____ years from this date (called "primary term"), and as long thereafter as oil, liquid hydrocarbons, gas or other respective constituent products, or any of them, is produced from said land or land with which said land is pooled.

In consideration of the premises the said lessee covenants and agrees:

1st. To deliver to the credit of lessor, free of cost, in the pipe line to which lessee may connect wells on said land, the equal one-eighth (⅛) part of all oil produced and saved from the leased premises.

2nd. To pay lessor for gas of whatsoever nature or kind produced and sold, or used off the premises, or used in the manufacture of any products therefrom, one-eighth (⅛), at the market price at the well, (but, as to gas sold by lessee, in no event more than one-eighth (⅛) of the proceeds received by lessee from such sales), for the gas sold, used off the premises, or in the manufacture of products therefrom, said payments to be made monthly. Where gas from a well producing gas only is not sold or used, lessee may pay or tender as royalty One Dollar ($1.00) per year per net mineral acre retained hereunder, and if such payment or tender is made it will be considered that gas is being produced within the meaning of the preceding paragraph.

This lease may be maintained during the primary term hereof without further payment or drilling operations. If the lessee shall commence to drill a well within the term of this lease or any extension thereof, the lessee shall have the right to drill such well to completion with reasonable diligence and dispatch, and if oil or gas, or either of them, be found in paying quantities, this lease shall continue and be in force with like effect as if such well had been completed within the term of years first mentioned.

If said lessor owns a less interest in the above described land than the entire and undivided fee simple estate therein, then the royalties herein provided for shall be paid the said lessor only in the proportion which lessor's interest bears to the whole and undivided fee.

Lessee shall have the right to use, free of cost, gas, oil and water produced on said land for lessee's operation thereon, except water from the wells of lessor.

When requested by lessor, lessee shall bury lessee's pipe lines below plow depth.

No well shall be drilled nearer than 200 feet to the house or barn now on said premises without written consent of lessor.

Lessee shall pay for damages caused by lessee's operations to growing crops on said land.

Lessee shall have the right at any time to remove all machinery and fixtures placed on said premises, including the right to draw and remove casing.

If the estate of either party hereto is assigned, and the privilege of assigning in whole or in part is expressly allowed, the covenants hereof shall extend to their heirs, executors, administrators, successors or assigns, but no change in the ownership of the land or assignment of rentals or royalties shall be binding on the lessee until after the lessee has been furnished with a written transfer or assignment or a true copy thereof. In case lessee assigns this lease, in whole or in part, lessee shall be relieved of all obligations with respect to the assigned portion or portions arising subsequent to the date of assignment.

Lessee may at any time execute and deliver to lessor or place of record a release or releases covering any portion or portions of the above described premises and thereby surrender this lease as to such portion or portions and be relieved of all obligations as to the acreage surrendered.

All express or implied covenants of this lease shall be subject to all Federal and State Laws, Executive Orders, Rules or Regulations, and this lease shall not be terminated, in whole or in part, nor lessee held liable in damages, for failure to comply therewith, if compliance is prevented by, or if such failure is the result of, any such Law, Order, Rule or Regulation.

Lessor hereby warrants and agrees to defend the title to the lands herein described, and agrees that the lessee shall have the right at any time to redeem for lessor, by payment, any mortgages, taxes or other liens on the above described lands, in the event of default of payment by lessor, and be subrogated to the rights of the holder thereof, and the undersigned lessors, for themselves and their heirs, successors and assigns, hereby surrender and release all right of dower and homestead in the premises described herein, in so far as said right of dower and homestead may in any way effect the purposes for which this lease is made, as recited herein.

Lessee, at its option, is hereby given the right and power to pool or combine the acreage covered by this lease or any portion thereof with other land, lease or leases in the immediate vicinity thereof, when in lessee's judgment it is necessary or advisable to do so in order to properly develop and operate said lease premises so as to promote the conservation of oil, gas or other minerals in and under and that may be produced from said premises, such pooling to be of tracts contiguous to one another and to be into a unit or units not exceeding 40 acres each in the event of an oil well, or into a unit or units not exceeding 640 acres each in the event of a gas well. Lessee shall execute in writing and record in the conveyance records of the county in which the land herein leased is situated an instrument identifying and describing the pooled acreage. The entire acreage so pooled into a tract or unit shall be treated, for all purposes except the payment of royalties on production from the pooled unit, as if it were included in this lease. If production is found on the pooled acreage, it shall be treated as if production is had from this lease, whether the well or wells be located on the premises covered by this lease or not. In lieu of the royalties elsewhere herein specified, lessor shall receive on production from a unit so pooled only such portion of the royalty stipulated herein as the amount of his acreage placed in the unit or his royalty interest therein on an acreage basis bears to the total acreage so pooled in the particular unit involved.

IN WITNESS WHEREOF, the undersigned execute this instrument as of the day and year first above written.
Witnesses:

_____

_____

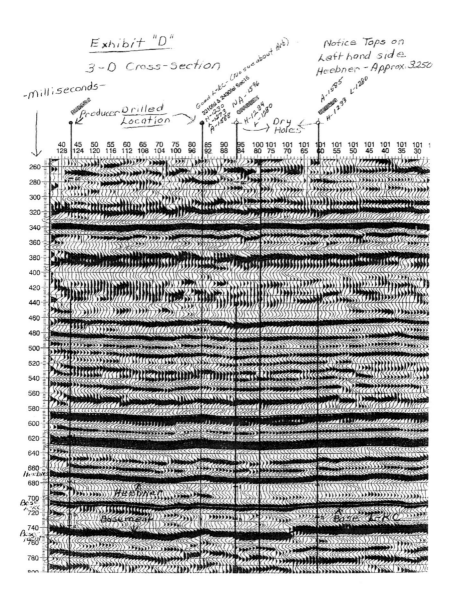

Exhibit "E"

Form C-1
March 2010
Form must be Typed
Form must be Signed
All blanks must be Filled

For KCC Use:
Effective Date: _____
District # _____
SGA7 ☐ Yes ☐ No

KANSAS CORPORATION COMMISSION
OIL & GAS CONSERVATION DIVISION

NOTICE OF INTENT TO DRILL
Must be approved by KCC five (5) days prior to commencing well
Form KSONA-1, Certification of Compliance with the Kansas Surface Owner Notification Act, MUST be submitted with this form.

Expected Spud Date: _____
  month   day   year

OPERATOR: License# _____
Name: _____
Address 1: _____
Address 2: _____
City: _____ State: _____ Zip: _____ +_____ ____
Contact Person: _____
Phone: _____

CONTRACTOR: License# _____
Name: _____

Well Drilled For:	Well Class:	Type Equipment:
☐ Oil	☐ Enh Rec ☐ Infield	☐ Mud Rotary
☐ Gas	☐ Storage ☐ Pool Ext.	☐ Air Rotary
	☐ Disposal ☐ Wildcat	☐ Cable
☐ Seismic : # of Holes	☐ Other	
☐ Other:		

☐ If OWWO: old well information as follows:

Operator: _____
Well Name: _____
Original Completion Date: _____ Original Total Depth: _____

Directional, Deviated or Horizontal wellbore? ☐ Yes ☐ No
If Yes, true vertical depth: _____
Bottom Hole Location: _____
KCC DKT #: _____

Spot Description:
_____ _____ - _____ - _____ Sec. _____ Twp. _____ S. R. _____ ☐ E ☐ W
_____ feet from ☐ N / ☐ S Line of Section
_____ feet from ☐ E / ☐ W Line of Section
Is SECTION: ☐ Regular ☐ Irregular?
(Note: Locate well on the Section Plat on reverse side)

County: _____
Lease Name: _____ Well #: _____
Field Name: _____
Is this a Prorated / Spaced Field? ☐ Yes ☐ No
Target Formation(s): _____
Nearest Lease or unit boundary line (in footage): _____
Ground Surface Elevation: _____ feet MSL
Water well within one-quarter mile: ☐ Yes ☐ No
Public water supply well within one mile: ☐ Yes ☐ No
Depth to bottom of fresh water: _____
Depth to bottom of usable water: _____
Surface Pipe by Alternate: ☐ I ☐ II
Length of Surface Pipe Planned to be set: _____
Length of Conductor Pipe (if any): _____
Projected Total Depth: _____
Formation at Total Depth: _____
Water Source for Drilling Operations:
☐ Well ☐ Farm Pond ☐ Other: _____
DWR Permit #: _____
(Note: Apply for Permit with DWR ☐*)*
Will Cores be taken? ☐ Yes ☐ No
If Yes, proposed zone: _____

AFFIDAVIT

The undersigned hereby affirms that the drilling, completion and eventual plugging of this well will comply with K.S.A. 55 et. seq.

It is agreed that the following minimum requirements will be met:

1. Notify the appropriate district office *prior* to spudding of well;
2. A copy of the approved notice of intent to drill *shall be* posted on each drilling rig;
3. The minimum amount of surface pipe as specified below *shall be set* by circulating cement to the top; in all cases surface pipe *shall be set* through all unconsolidated materials plus a minimum of 20 feet into the underlying formation.
4. If the well is dry hole, an agreement between the operator and the district office on plug length and placement is necessary *prior to plugging*;
5. The appropriate district office will be notified before well is either plugged or production casing is cemented in;
6. If an ALTERNATE II COMPLETION, production pipe shall be cemented from below any usable water to surface within *120 DAYS* of spud date. Or pursuant to Appendix "B" - Eastern Kansas surface casing order #133,891-C, which applies to the KCC District 3 area, alternate II cementing must be completed within 30 days of the spud date or the well shall be plugged. *In all cases, NOTIFY district office* prior to any cementing.

I hereby certify that the statements made herein are true and to the best of my knowledge and belief.

Date: _____ Signature of Operator or Agent: _____ Title: _____

For KCC Use ONLY
API # 15 - _____
Conductor pipe required _____ feet
Minimum surface pipe required _____ feet per ALT. ☐ I ☐ II
Approved by: _____
This authorization expires: _____
(This authorization void if drilling not started within 12 months of approval date.)
Spud date: _____ Agent: _____

Remember to:
- File Certification of Compliance with the Kansas Surface Owner Notification Act (KSONA-1) with Intent to Drill;
- File Drill Pit Application (form CDP-1) with Intent to Drill;
- File Completion Form ACO-1 within 120 days of spud date;
- File acreage attribution plat according to field proration orders;
- Notify appropriate district office 48 hours prior to workover or re-entry;
- Submit plugging report (CP-4) after plugging is completed (within 60 days);
- Obtain written approval before disposing or injecting salt water.
- If well will not be drilled or permit has expired (See: authorized expiration date) please check the box below and return to the address below.

☐ Well will not be drilled or Permit Expired Date: _____
Signature of Operator or Agent: _____

Mail to: KCC - Conservation Division,
130 S. Market - Room 2078, Wichita, Kansas 67202

Side Two

IN ALL CASES PLOT THE INTENDED WELL ON THE PLAT BELOW

In all cases, please fully complete this side of the form. Include items 1 through 5 at the bottom of this page.

Operator: _____

Lease: _____

Well Number: _____

Field: _____

Number of Acres attributable to well: _____

QTR/QTR/QTR/QTR of acreage: _____ - _____ - _____ - _____

Location of Well: County: _____

_____ feet from ☐ N / ☐ S Line of Section

_____ feet from ☐ E / ☐ W Line of Section

Sec _____ Twp. _____ S. R. _____ ☐ E ☐ W

Is Section: ☐ Regular or ☐ Irregular

If Section is Irregular, locate well from nearest corner boundary.

Section corner used: ☐ NE ☐ NW ☐ SE ☐ SW

PLAT

Show location of the well. Show footage to the nearest lease or unit boundary line. Show the predicted locations of lease roads, tank batteries, pipelines and electrical lines, as required by the Kansas Surface Owner Notice Act (House Bill 2032). You may attach a separate plat if desired.

LEGEND

O Well Location

☐ Tank Battery Location

—— Pipeline Location

------ Electric Line Location

▬▬ Lease Road Location

EXAMPLE

1980' FSL

SEWARD CO. 3390' FEL

NOTE: In all cases locate the spot of the proposed drilling location.

In plotting the proposed location of the well, **you must show:**

1. The manner in which you are using the depicted plat by identifying section lines. i.e. 1 section, 1 section with 8 surrounding sections, 4 sections, etc.

2. The distance of the proposed drilling location from the south / north and east / west outside section lines.

3. The distance to the nearest lease or unit boundary line (in footage).

4. If proposed location is located within a prorated or spaced field a certificate of acreage attribution plat must be attached: (C0-7 for oil wells; CG-8 for gas wells).

5. The predicted locations of lease roads, tank batteries, pipelines, and electrical lines.

TERRY W. PIESKER

KANSAS CORPORATION COMMISSION
OIL & GAS CONSERVATION DIVISION

Form CDP-1
May 2010
Form must be Typed

APPLICATION FOR SURFACE PIT

Submit in Duplicate

Operator Name:	License Number:

Operator Address:

Contact Person:	Phone Number:

Lease Name & Well No.:	Pit Location (QQQQ):

Type of Pit:	Pit is:	
☐ Emergency Pit ☐ Burn Pit	☐ Proposed ☐ Existing	Sec._____ Twp._____ R._____ ☐ East ☐ West
☐ Settling Pit ☐ Drilling Pit	If Existing, date constructed:	_____Feet from ☐ North / ☐ South Line of Section
☐ Workover Pit ☐ Haul-Off Pit		_____Feet from ☐ East / ☐ West Line of Section
(if WP Supply API No. or Year Drilled)	Pit capacity: _____(bbls)	_____County

Is the pit located in a Sensitive Ground Water Area? ☐ Yes ☐ No	Chloride concentration: _____ mg/l *(For Emergency Pits and Settling Pits only)*

Is the bottom below ground level? ☐ Yes ☐ No	Artificial Liner? ☐ Yes ☐ No	How is the pit lined if a plastic liner is not used?

Pit dimensions (all but working pits): _____Length (feet) _____Width (feet) ☐ N/A: Steel Pits
Depth from ground level to deepest point: _____(feet) ☐ No Pit

If the pit is lined give a brief description of the liner material, thickness and installation procedure.	Describe procedures for periodic maintenance and determining liner integrity, including any special monitoring.

Distance to nearest water well within one-mile of pit: _____feet Depth of water well _____feet	Depth to shallowest fresh water _____ feet. Source of information: ☐ measured ☐ well owner ☐ electric log ☐ KDWR

Emergency, Settling and Burn Pits ONLY:	Drilling, Workover and Haul-Off Pits ONLY:
Producing Formation: _____	Type of material utilized in drilling/workover: _____
Number of producing wells on lease: _____	Number of working pits to be utilized: _____
Barrels of fluid produced daily: _____	Abandonment procedure: _____
Does the slope from the tank battery allow all spilled fluids to flow into the pit? ☐ Yes ☐ No	Drill pits must be closed within 365 days of spud date.

I hereby certify that the above statements are true and correct to the best of my knowledge and belief.

_____ _____
Date   Signature of Applicant or Agent

KCC OFFICE USE ONLY	☐ Liner ☐ Steel Pit ☐ RFAC ☐ RFAS
Date Received: _____ Permit Number: _____	Permit Date: _____ Lease Inspection: ☐ Yes ☐ No

Mail to: KCC - Conservation Division, 130 S. Market - Room 2078, Wichita, Kansas 67202

THE INNER WORKINGS OF THE OIL AND GAS BUSINESS

KANSAS CORPORATION COMMISSION
OIL & GAS CONSERVATION DIVISION

Form KSONA-1
July 2010
Form Must Be Typed
Form must be Signed
All blanks must be Filled

CERTIFICATION OF COMPLIANCE WITH THE
KANSAS SURFACE OWNER NOTIFICATION ACT

*This form must be submitted with all Forms C-1 (Notice of Intent to Drill); CB-1 (Cathodic Protection Borehole Intent);
T-1 (Request for Change of Operator Transfer of Injection or Surface Pit Permit); and CP-1 (Well Plugging Application).
Any such form submitted without an accompanying Form KSONA-1 will be returned.*

Select the corresponding form being filed: ☒ C-1 (Intent) ☐ CB-1 (Cathodic Protection Borehole Intent) ☐ T-1 (Transfer) ☐ CP-1 (Plugging Application)

OPERATOR: License # _____

Name: _____

Address 1: _____

Address 2: _____

City: _____ State: _____ Zip: _____ + ___ ___ ___

Contact Person: _____

Phone: (_____) _____ Fax: (_____) _____

Email Address: _____

Well Location:

___ - ___ - ___ - ___ Sec. _____ Twp. _____ S. R. _____ ☐ East ☐ West

County: _____

Lease Name: _____ Well # : _____

*If filing a Form T-1 for multiple wells on a lease, enter the legal description of
the lease below:*

Surface Owner Information:

Name: _____

Address 1: _____

Address 2: _____

City: _____ State: _____ Zip: _____ + ___ ___ ___

*When filing a Form T-1 involving multiple surface owners, attach an additional
sheet listing all of the information to the left for each surface owner. Surface
owner information can be found in the records of the register of deeds for the
county, and in the real estate property tax records of the county treasurer.*

---

*If this form is being submitted with a Form C-1 (Intent) or CB-1 (Cathodic Protection Borehole Intent), you must supply the surface owners and
the KCC with a plat showing the predicted locations of lease roads, tank batteries, pipelines, and electrical lines. The locations shown on the plat
are preliminary non-binding estimates. The locations may be entered on the Form C-1 plat, Form CB-1 plat, or a separate plat may be submitted.*

Select one of the following:

☐ I certify that, pursuant to the Kansas Surface Owner Notice Act (House Bill 2032), I have provided the following to the surface
owner(s) of the land upon which the subject well is or will be located: 1) a copy of the Form C-1, Form CB-1, Form T-1, or Form
CP-1 that I am filing in connection with this form; 2) if the form being filed is a Form C-1 or Form CB-1, the plat(s) required by this
form; and 3) my operator name, address, phone number, fax, and email address.

☐ I have not provided this information to the surface owner(s). I acknowledge that, because I have not provided this information, the
KCC will be required to send this information to the surface owner(s). To mitigate the additional cost of the KCC performing this
task, I acknowledge that I am being charged a $30.00 handling fee, payable to the KCC, which is enclosed with this form.

*If choosing the second option, submit payment of the $30.00 handling fee with this form. If the fee is not received with this form, the KSONA-1
form and the associated Form C-1, Form CB-1, Form T-1, or Form CP-1 will be returned.*

I hereby certify that the statements made herein are true and correct to the best of my knowledge and belief.

Date: _____ Signature of Operator or Agent: _____ Title: _____

Mail to: KCC - Conservation Division, 130 S. Market - Room 2078, Wichita, Kansas 67202

2

Drilling of an Oil and Gas Well

The day has come to finally drill your first well. The drilling contractor will move the rig in and rig up. The first thing they will do is drill what we call a rathole. This is for the kelly, which will be used to drill each joint down as you go deeper and deeper. The kelly itself is a square piece of pipe about 6" × 6" and 50' long. There is a bushing attached to the kelly, which is about 1' × 1', that slides up and down on the kelly. This 1' × 1' bushing fits into the drilling table. The drilling table then rotates the kelly, drill pipe, and bit to make hole. You drill the kelly all the way down to the drilling table. Once this is done, you have to add another joint of drill pipe. Every time you make a connection or run a drill stem test, the kelly will be put down this rathole. In other words, this is a standby hole for the kelly when it is not in use. Depending on the rig, you may also drill what we call the mousehole, which is the place where they put the next joint of drill pipe to be added to the string as we go down the hole. Not all rigs in Kansas have this, but most of them do. This saves some time because you don't have to put the kelly in the rathole for every connection. You just unscrew it from the joint in the hole and screw the kelly right into the joint in the mousehole and add it to the string in the hole and start drilling again. Now you are ready to start making hole.

When we kick off drilling the hole, this is called spudding. We start out drilling 12 1/4" surface hole with a 12 1/4" bit. We drill down to whatever depth we plan on setting surface. This has been predetermined by what the state corporation commission recommends. In Kansas this is usually more than 200'. This surface pipe is to protect the freshwater zones from being contaminated. The 8 5/8" pipe is on location and has been tallied. Let's say it is 223.46' measured threads off, including the landing joint. We will drill the 12 1/4" hole to 225'. When we get to 225' we will condition the hole and come out, standing the drill pipe in the derrick and run the 8 5/8" casing. The casing has been run to bottom and a landing joint (short piece of 8 5/8" casing) has been put on top so that the 8 5/8" collar on the top joint is 2' to 3' below ground level. We now circulate the hole, which we call conditioning the hole, for about 30 minutes. We have called a cement crew to cement the surface pipe in place. Once the hole is in condition, the cementing crew will tie on to the 8 5/8" casing and begin mixing cement, usually around 150 sacks. This cement will go down the inside and back up the outside of the 8 5/8" casing to the top of the ground. The capacity of the 8 5/8" has been calculated by the cementer. Right behind the cement, after they have disconnected from the casing head and washed up all the cement in the lines and the pump, an 8 5/8' wiper plug is put in the top. They now reconnect to the well head and pump the plug down to almost bottom with water. Pressure is left on this, and the rig will be shut down for 8 hours, waiting on cement (WOC). We now have the surface pipe cemented from top to bottom on the outside. This is to protect the freshwater. The 8 hours downtime is to let the cement set up before we go back to drilling. Usually an accelerator is used, such as calcium, to quicken the setting time of the cement.

After 8 hours waiting time, we are ready to begin drilling a 7 7/8" hole. The landing joint is taken off, and a drilling nipple is put on top of the 8 5/8" casing so that the returns can get to surface and out to the drilling pits. Once we start drilling, we call this drilling under surface. Attached is diagram A of how it looks while we are drilling downhole.

Normally we drill this hole with water. The water is pumped down the drill pipe, and the samples are circulated to the top on the outside of the drill pipe. This is done for several hundred feet. In Kansas there is a very hard section, depending where you are in Kansas; it could be 600' to 2,200', which is a very good marker. This is called the anhydrite. It is the first marker (zone) that will be recorded. It is not a great indicator of how you will be running when you get to bottom because things can change a lot from there on down, but this marker will come into play later in this process.

Once we get to a couple of hundred feet above the estimated top of our first possible producing zones, we do what we call mud up. In this process, the water that we have been drilling with is displaced out of the hole, and drilling mud is put into the hole. This is done by the rig through the direction of an independent contractor called the mud company. Drilling mud is pumped down the inside of the drill pipe, and the samples are still circulated up the outside of the pipe just as before, except you have all the water out of the hole. This drilling mud brings up the samples much easier. In Kansas we run about 9# to 9.5# per gallon mud weight with a viscosity of around 40 to 50. This is monitored every tower. There are 3 crews of 4 men on each crew—morning tower, 11:00 p.m. to 7:00 a.m.; daylights 7:00 a.m. to 3:00 p.m.; and evening tower, 3:00 p.m. to 11:00 p.m. Also, a mud man from the mud contractor will monitor the mud daily and tell the drilling crews what he wants done. Mud, along with various other things like cottonseed hulls, are used to keep the walls from caving or various zones from taking fluid and losing circulation. It usually takes a couple of hours to displace the mud. Most rigs have a mud tank in which they have mixed the mud so they are ready to displace when they get to that point.

As you are drilling the well to total depth, you will encounter different rock formations. Diagram B depicts these formations as we drill downhole. In Western Kansas, on a normal well, the first zone of interest will usually be the Topeka. Thus, about 100' above your projected top of the Topeka, you will mud up. As mentioned before, this mud will help carry the formation samples. Your geologist has picked estimates of the formation tops of interest. He knows from the area about where to expect the different zones to come in. These are just estimates, but they are pretty good educated guesses. That's how he knows when he wants to mud up. He has usually sent orders out to the rig to mud up at a certain time, begin catching 10' wet and dry samples, and start keeping 1' drilling time. Samples are caught in what we call a sample box. As the fluid comes up the outside of the drill pipe and up to the surface, there is a V-shaped box that all the samples from the drilling process goes through. One of the four crew members is a sample catcher. As we drill down the hole, the sample catcher goes out and catches samples every 10'. This is only a small sample of the 10' area. Each time, after he catches the sample, he cleans out the box, which is where a small sampling of each 10' section is caught. He washes these samples up and cleans them with water. He takes a small sample, usually in a cup, out to the geologist so he can look at it through a microscope and describe what he sees. These are the wet samples. He is looking for shows of oil, types of rock, and various other things like porosity and denseness. He will write down a description of exactly what he sees. Also, as we are drilling, the rig is writing down exactly how long it takes to drill each foot. Each foot is timed on a geolograph located inside the doghouse. The geologist has what we call a strip log (a section of which you will find in exhibit E) with this drilling time graphed out for each foot. As he is drilling along, he writes down the description alongside the area he is looking at as they continue to drill down the hole. From looking at the drilling time, the geologist can usually call the tops of different formations. Drilling time is different for shale than it is for harder rock such as a limestone or dolomite. Thus, the change in time helps to indicate the top. You need to really know what you are doing to pick these tops because the changes are subtle and sometimes hard to correlate. We correlate these strip logs to other strip logs in the area as well as any logs from nearby wells. Usually, wells in the same areas look quite a bit alike. Hopefully you can find a strip log or open hole log or even a cased hole log of a well in the area. The way you correlate a log is not by total depth but by sea level. When the surveyor staked the location, he gave you an elevation above sea level to whatever your ground level elevation is for that exact location. This is called the ground level elevation. When the rig moved in, they have a small substructure with a floor on which the drilling table is located. As mentioned earlier, this table rotates the kelly to drill the hole. The kelly bushing fits into the table. The kelly bushing becomes the important measurement point. All subsea measurements for the well will be taken from the kelly bushing. Most kelly bushings in this area are 5' to 8' above ground level. Thus, this 5' to 8' must be added to the elevation to get a correct subsea elevation for all tops. All rig measurements will be from kelly bushing (KB). Now for the dry samples. They are cleaned and dried on a stove. These can be kept forever. If they are kept, they can be pulled out and looked at when you want to refer to them.

On the Central Kansas Uplift, most producing wells are located on what we call highs. Thus, the higher you are structurally, the better chance you have of getting a producing well. Usually, these highs or structures have what we call closure. Closure means the zone has limits and is isolated. Oil is a fossil fuel. It was produced by decaying fossils. One way to think of this, if you were a dinosaur, where would be the last place you would go if a flood was coming? To the highest point. This may not be how things came to be, but it makes it pretty simple to remember. Actually, lots of times this oil has migrated from some other place. Looking at the Lansing-Kansas City (diagram C) let me explain how you get the subsea tops (minus tops). Let's say the surface elevation of all four wells is 2,020' KB. Thus, on the surface, the land is flat. However, the top of the Lansing-Kansas City is not. Take well 1, a dry hole. The top of the Lansing was encountered at 3,255'. You subtract the KB of the well, 2,020', and you come up with -1,235. Look across to the other three wells and you see the actual top of each well. Since the all important reference point is sea level, the lower the number (minus) the higher the well. Thus, well 3 is 5' high to well 1. Well 2 is 15' high to the well 1. Well 1 is 10' high to well 4.

As I mentioned earlier, the geologist will look at all the samples and give a description of each sample. It's important that the geologist be on location during all drilling of productive zones. When you get to an area that might have a show of oil, the geologist will correlate the top and try to calculate where to drill to get through the zone of interest. At this point, the geologist will give the driller on the rig, a stop point. The rig will drill down to this point and stop. He will then pull the bit and drill pipe up about 1' off bottom and circulate the hole. The geologist will tell them to catch samples when they get to the stop point, 30 minutes after conditioning the hole, and 60 minutes after conditioning the hole.

When looking at samples, you need to remember it takes time to get the samples from the bottom of the hole to surface. Depending on the mud pump pressure, which will run somewhere around 800# to 1,000# in this area, this helps to determine the amount of time it takes to get what we call bottoms up. A good rule of thumb is 1 minute for every 100'. Thus, at 3,000', it would take approximately 30 minutes to get the sample from bottom to the top. By stopping and circulating the hole, you can look at a specific area or zone. You can determine if this zone has a chance of producing hydrocarbons. Remember, also, that some of the sample you are getting is what we call sluff. It is coming from cavings up the hole. You will always have samples coming, but they will become less once you have circulated in one spot for a while. Also, remember you are only getting a small sample of the zone in your little cup, so you are only seeing a small part of what you have actually cut. Now, say you had a nice show of oil in your sample of a zone. You may want to test this area. This can be done by a drill stem test (DST).

As the geologist is looking at samples while drilling, he can correlate the 10' samples back, using the drill time, to figure exactly where the samples came from in the well. This is called lag time. Say you have a sample at 3,000'. You count back 30 minutes on the strip log from the minutes drilled, and this is the approximate place that the sample came from. He will then write the sample description alongside this area of the strip log.

As you are drilling along, certain types of formations drill differently. A rather thick shale, say 4' to 6' thick, will drill fairly quickly, say 2 minutes per foot. A limestone, if dense, may drill from 3 minutes to 5 minutes. To correlate the drilling time to another open hole or cased hole log, you can slide the strip log up and down, depending on how it is running to the other well. The different formations or zones, usually run pretty much the same in general areas. In other words, when you have some control wells, old wells in the general area, it is pretty easy to correlate one with the other. When this can get complicated is when you are drilling a wildcat well. This is a well that is approximately one mile away from any previous well. Even at this distance, a well can be correlated; it just may have a few subtle changes in drilling time and zones.

As you are moving downhole, going by the different formations, you are correlating to some nearby well, either with a log or a strip log, and you know how you are running in relation to that well. Hopefully you are running high, which means your tops for the different formations are higher in the well you are drilling. By high, I don't mean 30 or 40 feet. Structure in this area is very subtle. Lots of times 2' to 3' is very good. It only takes that much to make a producing well versus a dry hole. When you are running high, the excitement becomes great.

While drilling up potential zones, you are looking for changes in drilling time through the zones. We call these changes in drilling time drilling breaks. In other words, we want to see drilling times of less than 1 minute to 2 minutes, where we might normally see 3 to 5 minutes per foot. This is an indication or porosity, which means the rocks are porous and could contain hydrocarbons. This, along with oil shows, could indicate a productive zone of interest.

Here are some things you need for a productive zone: porosity, the ability of the rock to hold hydrocarbons, and permeability, the ability of the hydrocarbon to flow through the rock to the well bore. This can best be determined by the flow pressure on a DST or the micro log. Both of these are very important to a productive well. Also, the bottom-hole pressure of the reservoir is very important. It too can be determined by a drill stem test. The micro log will determine the exact location of the permeability. You can have permeability without porosity. In this case, more than likely, you would have a fracture. You can see this on a micro log, where you may have very little show of oil or change in drilling time. A micro log is one of the most valuable tools we have and should be run on every well.

Now take a look at the drill stem test (DST), as depicted in diagram D. Once you have located a zone of interest, you call a tester to run a drill stem test over a small section of what you have just drilled and looked at. You have looked at the rocks, and you think there is some potential to produce oil or gas. The bit and drill pipe are pulled out of the hole and put in the derrick once you have run what we call a short trip. In other words, you have drilled several hundred feet and the walls of the well may not be very clean. The hole may be sticky. In order to clean up the hole, we usually pull the bit and drill pipe up about halfway out of the hole and run back to bottom and circulate the hole clean. Doing this, you have knocked off some of the old cuttings and heavy mud that did not make it to the surface. This will make it a lot easier to run the DST tool and cut down on the chances of getting stuck or not making it to bottom. This is usually done on the first DST and will not have to be done on future tests.

Once you are back on bottom and right before you are ready to come out of the hole with the bit and drill pipe, you drop a sure shot down the inside of the drill pipe. The sure shot will fall to bottom and determine how straight the hole is. Most drilling company contracts state that the hole can be no more than 3 to 5 degrees off at the most, or the hole should be plugged and a new hole drilled. When we are talking 3 to 5 degrees, we mean the hole is not straight. It is off 5 degrees at the bottom in one direction or the other. Usually the well may be 1 or 2 degrees off at the most. The drill pipe and bit are then pulled, and the sure shot is taken out and read. This is usually done when surface is set and at least once while you're going downhole. It is probably a good thing to do any time you pull the drill pipe out of the hole. Also, as a check to make sure your depths are correct, you measure the pipe as you pull it out of the hole. This is called strapping the pipe. This is just a good check on the rig to make sure your depths are correct. This is usually done the first time you come out of the hole while drilling on bottom. The tally will either be short or long. Hopefully, if everything is correct, it won't be off much. This usually depends whether the rig is a good rig or a bad rig.

Now we have the drill pipe and bit on surface for the DST. The geologist has determined a hard spot above the zone to be tested to set the packer. Usually two packers are run on the top in case one does not hold. They are usually 5' apart. The distance from the bottom packer to TD is figured, and pipe is run below the two packers. This is called the anchor. Some of this pipe will have perforations (holes) so that fluid can enter the drill pipe. This is called the tool. Instruments to record time, flow pressures, and bottom-hole pressure are run in the DST tool. Usually two instruments are run, so if one does not work correctly, you will have a backup. The tool is put together and run in to bottom on the drill pipe. It has been calculated by the tester exactly where it should hit when it gets to bottom. The bottom of the tail-pipe (pipe below the packers) is set on bottom, and the tool is opened hydraulically by the weight of the drill pipe. This usually takes less than a minute once you are on bottom. The inside of the drill pipe is empty when it gets to bottom. Once the tool is opened, fluid from the packer to bottom is allowed to flow into the drill pipe. Looking below the drilling floor, the backside of the drill pipe and the hole should stay full of fluid (mud). This tells you that the packers are holding. If fluid is not at the surface on the backside, you have a packer failure, and the test will be no good. You can start out of the hole. You have what they call a miss run.

Once the tool is opened, the tester has run a hose from the top connection on the drill pipe that will be run into a 5-gallon bucket of water on the drilling floor. When the tool is opened, the inside of the drill pipe begins filling up with fluid and pushing air out the top into this bucket, which is full of water. The air coming out will make bubbles in the water. This is called the bubble bucket. Depending on how fast this builds, as you push the hose further and further into the bucket, determines the amount of time that you leave the tool open. This time usually goes from 15 minutes, if it builds fast to the bottom, to 1 hour to 1 1/2 hours, if it builds slowly. After this first initial flow (IF), the tool is closed so that the pressure builds up and is recorded. The drill pipe will be rotated to close the tool. This shut-in usually lasts about twice as long as the opening. The hose in the bubble bucket is bled off and then reopened and checked to see if it blows again. If it does, we call this blow back (BB), and this is usually a good indication that we have some gas in the pipe. This is called the initial shut-in and will give you an initial shut-in pressure (ISIP). The tool is then opened again for a second flow period, which we call the final flow (FF), by rotating the drill pipe. It again should build up in the bubble bucket, which will again determine the amount of time it will be opened. After that, the tool is shut in once more by rotating the drill pipe. This is called the final shut-in. This will give you a final shut-in pressure (FSIP). Again you will watch the bubble bucket for blow back. After the tool has been on bottom for the second shut-in period, the drill pipe is started out of the hole. The drill stem test will last anywhere from 3 hours to 6 hours on bottom. As the pipe is pulled out of the hole, it is checked by smell for any gas. Once fluid is encountered, samples are collected and evaluated for oil, mud, gas, and water. The exact amount of each type of fluid is recorded along with gas. A sample of each stand (joint of pipe) is taken. For example, once the test is out of the hole, let's say you recovered 250' gas in the pipe (GIP), 200' clean gassy oil (CGO); 120' heavy oil cut mud (HOCM), 60% oil and 40% mud; 120' oil cut muddy water (OCMW), 10% oil, 20% mud, 70% water. The tester will then tear down the tool and pull out the recorders and interpret the flow charts. If everything worked correctly, the flow charts will look exactly the same. The charts are read by the tester. They record the following (exhibit F is attached, a copy of a drill stem test chart):

> first opening—initial flow (IF)
> first shut-in—initial shut-in pressure (ISIP)
> second opening—final flow (FF)
> second shut-in—final shut-in pressure (FSIP)

Let me go through each of these. First, the IF, say your initial flow was 120# to 195#. This tells you that you have good drive or permeability. Secondly, I'd look at the FF pressures, say 195# to 250#. This is good. They are still building. Now I look at the shut-in pressures. Let's say the ISIP is 1,057#, and the FSIP is 1,049#. This is good. This tells me that the reservoir is fairly good sized. There was very little drop from the first shut-in to the second shut-in. In other words, the drop was minimal. Now let's say the FSIP was 800#. This would scare me. That's more than a 20% drop in just a short time. My personal opinion is that I do not like to see much over a 10% drop at the most. This tells me that the reservoir might be limited.

This gives you a quick overview of the DST. Exhibit F is a copy of a drill stem test report. Every zone that has a possibility of producing should probably be tested. You can also put two or three zones together, but you don't want to get your anchor too long. After you have run the test, you go back to bottom and condition the hole an hour to get anything you have knocked off the walls out of the hole, and you go back to drilling for the next zone. Depending on the area, you may run as many as 7 or 8 tests. They are expensive, but you know what you have when you get done. The DST results can be calculated out to give you some idea what this well will produce when you get it on.

The well is then drilled to TD. Once TD has been reached, the hole is conditioned, and a complete set of open hole logs should be run. There are several possibilities. I usually run a dual induction, neutron/density porosity log, and a micro log. In Kansas, I believe you could get by with a radiation guard log (RAG) instead of the dual and porosity logs, but I would always run a micro log. I'll get into the logs in detail later. Once the logs are out, they need to be evaluated through your productive zones, and also see if you might have missed something on the way down the hole. If you missed something, you can go back and run what we call a straddle test. This entails isolating the bottom with another packer and running tailpipe below it to bottom with the top packers just like a regular test. If you find something way up the hole, once in a while you can run what we call a hook wall packer on bottom without running tailpipe clear to bottom. The success rate on these is far less than with running tailpipe. Oftentimes the lower packer will not hold. The hook slips and you get an invalid test. You cannot monitor this from the surface like you can the top packers.

Once you have evaluated everything, it is decision time. Do we plug this well or run pipe? This can be the toughest decision of all. Will this well make enough oil or gas to pay for itself in a certain amount of time? At $70 per barrel, you need around 6,000 barrels to pay this well off. The worst thing you can do for yourself and investors is set pipe on a well that will only make 3,000 barrels of oil over a 5-year period. That's a loser.

Major things that you want to try to avoid when drilling a well are losing circulation and getting stuck. A good mud man will keep you out of a lot of trouble, along with a good pusher and drilling company. The drilling company needs to have good people and good equipment. You need a good mud pump and good drill pipe. Drill pipe that is thin and weak will cause you to have holes and get stuck very easily. If you are drilling along and your samples become very weak or not a lot of sample, you may have a hole in the pipe. You need to get the pipe out of the hole as soon as possible. If you don't, you will be stuck.

Diagram "A"
Drilling Operation

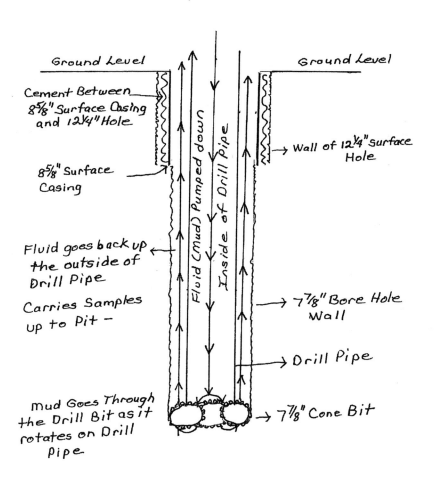

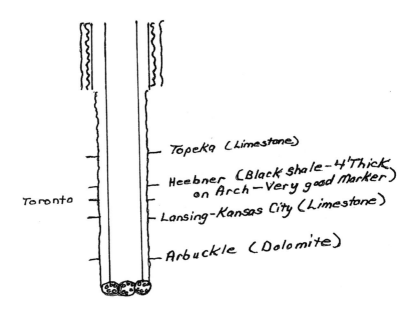

Diagram "B"

Kansas Zones of Interest

Topeka (Limestone)

Heebner (Black shale-4'Thick on Arch—Very good Marker)

Toronto

Lansing-Kansas City (Limestone)

Arbuckle (Dolomite)

Diagram "C"

Under Ground View

Lansing-Kansas City
(L-KC)

-Legend-
Ory Hole
• Producer

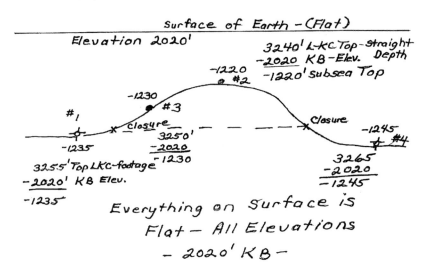

Surface of Earth - (Flat)

Elevation 2020'

3240' L-KC Top - straight
-2020 KB - Elev. Depth
-1220' subsea Top

-1220
@ #2

-1230

#1

#3

closure
3250'

Closure

-1245

#4

-1235

-2020
-1230

3265
-2020
-1245

3255' Top LKC-footage
-2020' KB Elev.

-1235

Everything on Surface is
Flat — All Elevations
— 2020' KB —

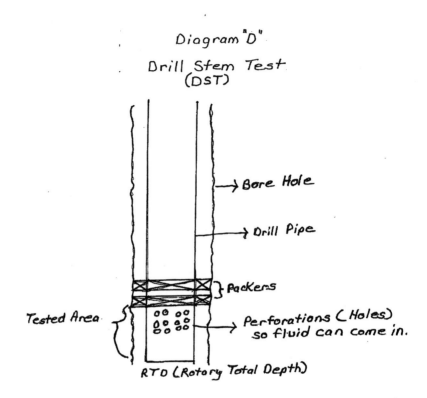

Diagram "D"

Drill Stem Test
(DST)

Bore Hole

Drill Pipe

Packers

Tested Area

Perforations (Holes)
so fluid can come in.

RTD (Rotary Total Depth)

The Packers are hydraulically set against
the Well Bore Hole Walls. Only the
hole below the Packers will be
tested. Packers must be set in hard
formation so they do not leak past.

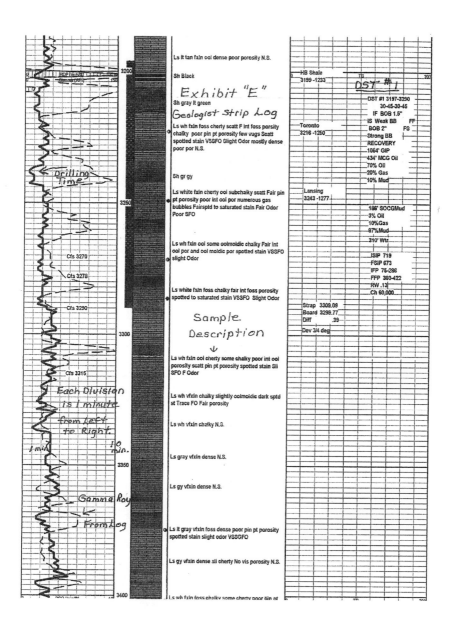

Ls lt tan fxln ool dense poor porosity N.S.

Sh Black

Exhibit "E"

Sh gray lt green

Geologist Strip Log

Ls wh fxln foss cherty scatt F int foss porsity chalky poor pin pt porosity few vugs Scatt spotted stain VSSFO Slight Odor mostly dense poor por N.S.

Sh gr gy

Ls white fxln cherty ool subchalky scatt Fair pin pt porosity poor int ool por numerous gas bubbles Fairsptd to saturated stain Fair Odor Poor SFO

Ls wh fxln ool some oolmoldic chalky Fair int ool por and ool moldic por spotted stain VSSFO slight Odor

Ls white fxln foss chalky fair int foss porosity spotted to saturated stain VSSFO Slight Odor

Sample Description

↓

Ls wh fxln ool cherty some chalky poor int ool porosity scatt pin pt porosity spotted stain Sli SFO F Odor

Ls wh vfxln chalky slightly oolmoldic dark sptd st Trace FO Fair porosity

Ls wh vfxln chalky N.S.

Ls gray vfxln dense N.S.

Ls gy vfxln dense N.S.

Ls lt gray vfxln foss dense poor pin pt porosity spotted stain slight odor VSSGFO

Ls gy vfxln dense sli cherty No vis porosity N.S.

Ls wh fxln foss chalky some cherty poor pin pt

HB Shale
3199 -1233

Toronto
3216 -1250

Lansing
3243 -1277

Strap 3309.09
Board 3299.77
Diff .39
Dev 3/4 deg

DST #1

DST #1 3197-3290
30-45-30-45
IF BOB 1.5"
IS Weak BB   FF
BOB 2"   FG
Strong BB
RECOVERY
1054' GIP
434' MCG Oil
70% Oil
20% Gas
10% Mud

186' SOCGMud
3% Oil
10%Gas
87%Mud
310' Wtr

ISIP 719
FSIP 673
IFP 75-286
FFP 303-422
RW .13
Ch 60,000

Drilling Time

Cts 3270

Cts 3278

Cts 3290

Cts 3315

Each Division is 1 minute from Left to Right.

1 min.   10 min.

Gamma Ray From Log

3200

3250

3300

3350

3400

Exhibit "F"

DRILL STEM TEST REPORT

TRILOBITE TESTING, INC

Po Box 550
Hays Ks 67601

ATTN: Terry Piesker

20 15 18 Ellis KS

Job Ticket: 38133   DST#: 3

Test Start: 2010.02.17 @ 13:12:13

GENERAL INFORMATION:

Drill Stem Test Chart

Formation:	Arbuckle	
Deviated:	No Whipstock:	ft (KB)
Time Tool Opened:	14:49:13	
Time Test Ended:	19:05:43	
Interval:	3510.00 ft (KB) To 3553.00 ft (KB) (TVD)	
Total Depth:	3553.00 ft (KB) (TVD)	
Hole Diameter:	7.88 inchesHole Condition: Good	

Test Type:	Conventional Bottom Hole
Tester:	Dan Bangle
Unit No:	38
Reference Elevations:	1966.00 ft (KB)
	1958.00 ft (CF)
KB to GR/CF:	8.00 ft

Serial #: 8354   Inside

Press@RunDepth:	159.64 psig @	3517.00 ft (KB)
Start Date:	2010.02.17	End Date: 2010.02.17
Start Time:	13:12:14	End Time: 19:05:43

Capacity:	8000.00 psig
Last Calb.:	2010.02.17
Time On Btm:	2010.02.17 @ 14:48:43
Time Off Btm:	2010.02.17 @ 17:20:13

TEST COMMENT: F-Strong B-B in 11 min
ISI-Weak steady surface blow
FF-Strong B-B in 11 min
FSI-Weak steady surface blow

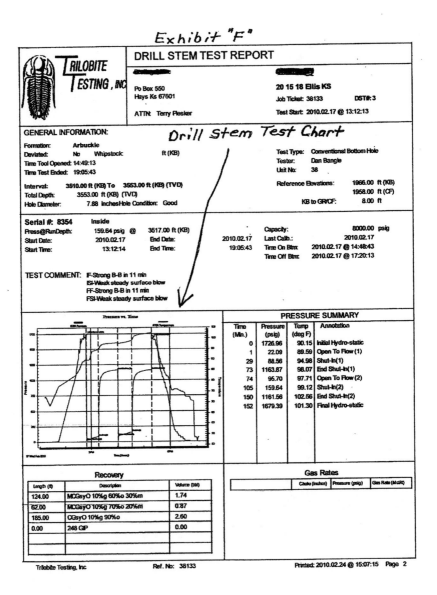

PRESSURE SUMMARY

Time (Min.)	Pressure (psig)	Temp (deg F)	Annotation
0	1726.96	90.15	Initial Hydro-static
1	22.09	89.59	Open To Flow (1)
29	88.56	94.98	Shut-In(1)
73	1163.87	98.07	End Shut-In(1)
74	95.70	97.71	Open To Flow (2)
105	159.64	99.12	Shut-In(2)
150	1161.56	102.56	End Shut-In(2)
152	1679.39	101.30	Final Hydro-static

Recovery

Length (ft)	Description	Volume (bbl)
124.00	MCGsyO 10%g 60%o 30%m	1.74
62.00	MCGsyO 10%o 70%o 20%m	0.87
185.00	CGsyO 10%g 90%o	2.60
0.00	248 GIP	0.00

Gas Rates

Choke (Inches)	Pressure (psig)	Gas Rate (Mcf/d)

Trilobite Testing, Inc   Ref. No: 38133   Printed: 2010.02.24 @ 15:07:15   Page 2

44

3

Logging

Open Hole Logs

There are two basic types of logs, open hole and cased hole. Open hole logs are logs that are run before casing is set, usually when the well has been drilled to rotary total depth (RTD). Cased hole logs are run after the casing has been set.

First, let me explain the open hole logs. There are many types of logs. These are run to help determine the possibility of making a commercial oil or gas well. Several logs are needed to make this determination. These groups of logs, called a suite, when looked at in the proper prospective, can give you a good idea of what you have. There is no one log that can do all this by itself. It takes a combination of logs to give you the whole picture. In respect to Kansas, these logs, along with the drill stem tests on the well, can give you an excellent idea of what kind of well you end up with.

I run a set of three logs on most wells with an additional log, the sonic log, on the first well drilled on every 3-D project. The three main logs that I run are the neutron/density porosity log, dual induction log, and the micro log. Let me explain how each of these works and a little bit about how you interpret them.

First of all, on the left-hand side of all of these logs, you will find a gamma ray log. The gamma ray log measures radioactivity to determine what types of rocks are present in the well bore. Because shale contain radioactive elements, they emit lots of gamma rays. On the other hand, limestone, dolomites, and sandstones emit very few gamma rays. This makes it fairly easy to determine zones of interest. Basically you are trying to determine what is shale and what is nonshale. This gamma ray log does this very nicely. The logging tool is lowered into the well bore on a wire line. It is lowered to the bottom of the hole. Once it is on bottom, the tool is turned on and the tool is pulled up the hole slowly, recording measurements at half-foot intervals and in API units. Shale have elevated levels of radiation. Limestone and dolomites, when clean, usually have very low levels of radiation. Sandstone is usually somewhere in between. You can take a look at any of the first four exhibits, A through D, and see exactly how you determine the difference between shale, sandstones, limestone, and dolomites.

Now that we have the gamma ray log figured out, let's take a look at the compensated neutron/density log, exhibit A. You see the gamma ray on the left-hand side of the log. Now notice the dotted line that runs down the left edge of the log, about two divisions from the left edge. This is the caliper log. There are ten divisions from the left to the right side on this log. The far-left division is 6", and the far-right division is 16". In other words, each division represents 1" from left to right. Notice the dark line running down the log just to the left of the 8" division. This would represent the borehole size, 7 7/8". Remember, we used a 7 7/8' bit to drill this well. The caliper tells you what the hole size is at any given point on the log. When the caliper goes to the left of the borehole line, this means it has wall cake. When it comes to the right side of the borehole line, it means the borehole has been washed out. Usually, you only see wall cake where you have a possible zone of interest. Wall cake is our first indicator of permeability. Permeability is the ability of a fluid to flow through a rock. This fluid can be anything from water, oil, or gas.

Now going back to the gamma ray, notice that the units are measured from 0 on the left to 150 units on the right. Thus, limestone, dolomites, and sands are on the left with shale being on the right-hand side. Notice the Heebner on the log. This is a 4' thick shale, which is a great marker on the Central Kansas Uplift. This is really helpful to a geologist who sets on any well. Right below this, you see about a 10' shale and then a limestone, about 8' to 10' thick. The very top of this, where it moves over to the left and cleans up, we call this the top of the Toronto. You then go into another shale for about 12' to 14' and then into the top of the Lansing-Kansas City. The Lansing-Kansas City section is 240' to 260' thick. There are several zones in the Lansing-Kansas City on the Arch (Central Kansas Uplift). We letter them from the *A* through the *K* or *L*, depending on the area. All of these zones can be productive. Usually you will only have one or two that produce, unless you're lucky. I have seen as many as eight produce oil in the same well.

Now for the right-hand side of the neutron/density log. This is the porosity side of the log. You have a neutron porosity that is determined by assuming that the reservoir pore spaces are filled with either water or oil and then measuring the amount of hydrogen atoms (neutrons) in the pores. When you are in a gas well, this log will underestimate porosity in a gas zone. Density logging determines the rock bulk density along the well bore. This is the overall density of a rock including solid matrix and the fluid enclosed in the pores. Geologically, bulk density is a function of the density of the minerals forming a rock (i.e., matrix) and the enclosed volume of free fluids (porosity). This is done by a radioactive source applied to the hole wall that emits medium energy gamma rays into the formation so these gamma rays may be thought of as high-velocity particles that collide with the electrons in the formation. At each collision the gamma ray loses some of its energy to the electron and then continues with diminished energy. This interaction is known as Compton scattering. The scattered gamma rays reaching the detector at the fixed station from the source are counted as an indication of formation density. All of this is done through the computer. If you are interested, there are formulas that are used to determine all this. The most important thing we need to know is what kind of matrix the log is run on. The following are the matrix values for each type of rock:

> quartz sand—2.65
> limey, arkosk, or shaly sand—2.68
> limestone—2.71
> dolomite—2.87

Now, looking at exhibit A, the dotted line is neutron porosity. The solid line is density porosity. The porosity scale goes from –10% on the right-hand side to 30% on the left-hand side. Each division is 2% porosity. Look at 3,408' on the porosity log. The neutron porosity is 17%, and the density porosity is 16%. Basically, you can take an average of the two, which would be 16.5% porosity. The dotted line to the far right is a correction device that is used if you really want to get technical. This log was run on a 2.71 limestone matrix, and that is what you have in the Lansing-Kansas City limestone. When you get into the Arbuckle, which is a dolomite, it should be run on a 2.81 to 2.87 matrix. This would make a lot of difference in the porosity. As I mentioned earlier, this is a great tool in gas because it causes the lines to go in completely different directions; in other words, it makes them cross over each other. This log tells you the porosity of your zones.

The second log is the dual induction log, exhibit B. Notice the left-hand side has the same gamma ray on it. Now let's look at the dark dotted line on the left-hand side. This is called the spontaneous potential (SP). This log characterizes rock formation properties. This log works by measuring small electric potentials (measured in millivolts) between depths in the borehole and a grounded voltage at the surface. The change in voltage through the well bore is caused by the buildup of charge on the well bore walls. Clays and shale, composed predominately of clays, will generate one charge, and permeable formations such as sandstone, limestone, and dolomites will generate an opposite one. The SP will vary from formation to formation and will not give a definite answer to how permeable or the porosity of the formation that it is logging. The SP tool is one of the simplest tools. SP data can be used to find the following:

Where permeable formations are
The boundaries of these formations
Correlation of formations when compared with data from other analogue wells
Values for the formation, water resistivity

Drilling mud salinity (usually freshwater mud) will affect the strength of the electromotive forces that give the SP deflections. Personally, I do not use this curve other than to help indicate a possible zone, which I would see on other logs I am running. To me this is nothing more than a throw-in log. It's not of much value to me.

Now look at the right-hand side of the dual induction log. You have three lines: a solid line, small dash line, and a large dash line. These are called resistivity curves. Resistivity logging is a method of logging that works by characterizing the rock or sediment in the borehole by measuring its electric resistivity. Resistivity is a fundamental material property that represents how strongly a material opposes the flow of electric current. Resistivity is measured using four electrical probes to eliminate the resistance of the contact leads. It must be run in holes containing electrically conductive mud or water. Most rock materials are insulators, while their enclosed fluids are conductors. Hydrocarbons are an exception because they are almost infinitely resistive. When a formation is porous and contains salt water, the overall resistivity will be low. When the formation contains hydrocarbons or low porosity, its resistivity will be high. High resistivity values may indicate a hydrocarbon-bearing formation. While you are drilling, drilling fluids will invade the formation, changing the resistivity measured by the tool in the invaded zone. For this reason, several resistivity tools with different investigation lengths are used to measure the formation density. That's why you have three curves, as mentioned above. The dark line is the shallow resistivity, the small dashed line is the medium distance curve, and the long dashed line is the deep distance curve. In other words, the deep gets out into virgin territory that has not been invaded by drilling fluids. Resistivity is measured in ohms, from .2 on the left-hand side, to 2,000 on the right-hand side.

Take a look at the zone from 3,354' to 3,373' in exhibit B. At 3,360' the deep reads 40 ohms, at 3,366' it reads 50 ohms, and at

3,370' it reads 100 ohms. Immediately, you consider this to be a possible hydrocarbon-bearing zone. Now move down to 3,393' to 3,400'. Look around 3,397', which reads 11 ohms. More than likely, this is going to be water or what we call wet. Now go down to 3,440' to 3,450'. Notice that this is a shale, from the gamma ray curve on the left, and a shale will have very low resistivity—4 ohms. Also, notice the SP curve (dotted line on the left-hand side of the borehole). See how it juts to the left in possible zones and to the right in shale. This log helps to determine the type of rock you are looking at.

Before I move on, let me explain one real problem with the dual induction log being used in parts of Kansas. This log was made and used in Texas and Oklahoma, where they have very thick productive zones. This is a great tool for that area. However, in Kansas, we often have very thin zones, 2' to 8' often at the most. What happens is that this log does not always have enough reaction time to give an accurate reading on a very thin zone. This is something to keep in mind when you are reading these logs in this area.

In Kansas, in the past, the major log we use to run is what they call a RAG log. This log has a gamma ray log on the left-hand side, just like all the other logs. On the right-hand side you have a neutron porosity curve and a resistivity curve. The resistivity curve is the same as the medium curve on the dual induction log. Attached is exhibit E. I have marked a couple of spots that look good on this log. Notice, when you get the porosity up (to the left) and the resistivity up (to the right), this would definitely have some possibilities. One thing to keep in mind about this log is the fact that it can be highly optimistic. Some of this is due to the fact that it is a medium curve. Also, neutron porosity can be optimistic. You are actually looking for separation between the lines going in opposite directions. This may be as good a log as the dual induction and the neutron/density log, as far as Kansas is concerned.

The final log I run is the micro log. This is a permeability log. Permeability is the ability of a fluid to flow through a rock. This log is attached in exhibit C. This is one of the most important logs we have in Kansas. Due to the thin zones we have in Kansas, this log really comes in handy. Also, it is great in the Arbuckle, where you are looking for permeability without getting into water. Oftentimes the Arbuckle will have wall cake all the way through it, but without this log, it is almost impossible to find the permeable sections.

Notice in exhibit C that you have the gamma ray log and the caliper log on the left-hand side of the log. Now look at the right-hand side of the log. This is a type of resistivity log. The measurements are from 0 on the left to 20 ohms on the right-hand side of the log. The dark line on the log has an investigative depth of 1.5", and the dotted line has an investigative depth of 2". This log will give you some idea of permeability. It won't tell you what kind of fluid it is, but it will tell you that you have a good chance of getting some kind of fluid. The 1.5" line will read in lower ohms than the 2" reading when you have permeability. Thus the lines will cross over each other. Thus, this is one of the easiest logs of all to read. You are basically looking for crossover, where the solid line goes to the left of the dotted line (the shaded area). The further to the left the solid line is, the better. Also, the more separation between the lines, the better. This is an excellent log for Arbuckle evaluation. As mentioned earlier, the caliper log and wall cake are an indication of permeability. With this log you can actually pinpoint the perm in the Arbuckle. It can make the difference between an oil completion or a water well. The micro log is an excellent log for the thin Lansing-Kansas City zones we have in Kansas. This is one of my favorite logs.

The last log that I use is the sonic log, exhibit D. The sonic log shows a formations interval transit time, which is the measure of the formations capacity to transmit sound waves. Quantitatively, the sonic log evaluates porosity in liquid filled pores. I personally, do not use this log for much. This log is usually run on the first well on a 3-D project area so that the geophysicist can make sure his markers are correct with regard to the project.

Cased Hole Logs

Cased hole logs are logs that are run after the well has been cased. I run what we call a correlation bond log. This is a gamma ray log on the left-hand side, just like the open hole log. The depths are correlated to the open hole log, which is the bible for this well. Most loggers are smart enough to tie everything in correctly, but you should always check it out for yourself and make sure things have been tied in correctly. This is very important when it comes to shooting the zone out. Attached, diagram F, is a copy of the correlation bond log.

Also, on the left-hand side, you see a dark line running down the log with dark marks across the paper every forty feet or so. This is the collar log. You use these collars to tie into when you get ready to perforate the well. These tie you directly into the well bore. These collars will never change. This log will be used for the duration of the well.

Now for the right-hand side of the log. The dark line closest to the well bore in most places is the bonding tool. This gives you a good idea if the pipe is bonded. By bonding, we mean it has cement around it. The dotted line is travel time. This tool uses sound to tell if there is cement on the outside of the pipe. I think of it as if there was a man with a hammer tapping on the pipe, something like looking for a stud in your wall. Where it has a hollow sound, there is not a stud. When it has a solid sound, you are on a stud. This dotted line often runs a lot like your gamma ray, where your shale go to the left and your zones go over to the right if they have good bonding. Most people in the industry very seldom look at the travel time. They are most interested in the bonding line. You will notice that every so often you get a little blip where the bonding line moves away from the borehole. This does not always mean bad bonding. What happens is that the zone is so hard, the rock in the formation, that it appears that it is not bonded. Most of the time this is not the case if the zone was very hard with no porosity. It is a false echo. You can usually tell this by going through your open hole logs and determining that the zone is very hard. Also, oftentimes you will not get a good bond when you have an oil zone. In theory, oil will not bond to cement, thus you should not have bonding across a good oil zone. Most of the time this is not the case because the oil zone has been invaded with drilling mud. Thus, you will get some bonding. I am sure if we had overpressured zones this probably would not be the case. There are very few overpressured zones in Kansas. You would probably find these types of zones in big-oil country in Texas and Oklahoma. By overpressured I mean that the bottom-hole pressure is such that the well would flow on its own if it were not for the weight of the mud in the hole. Mud weight in deep-hole country is used to control the well while drilling. If not for heavy mud weights, many wells in the southern part of the United States would go out of control. In other words, you would have blowouts.

This should give you a good idea what you can do with different types of logs. Logs are very useful, but they alone are not the answer to whether you want to set pipe on a well or not. You need to use these logs in conjunction with your DSTs. This way you do not get fooled. I have seen logs in Kansas that calculate wet when there is no water at all. What usually happens in these kinds of areas, the parameters are changed. You use a different RW factor so that the calculations come out correct. In my opinion, this is like cheating. That is why you need to use different things to determine a pipe setter. Logging is definitely not an exact science. Logs can and do lie.

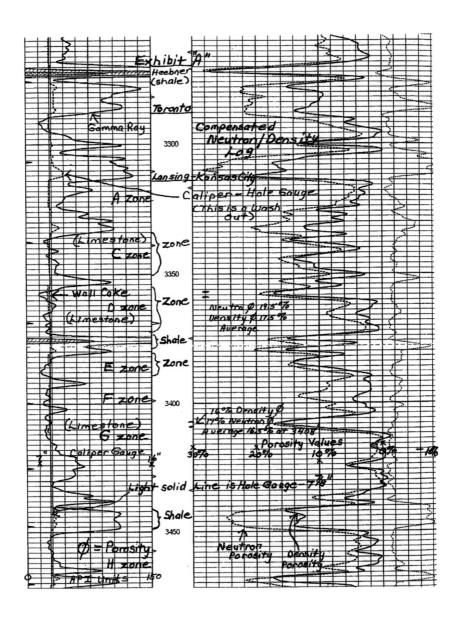

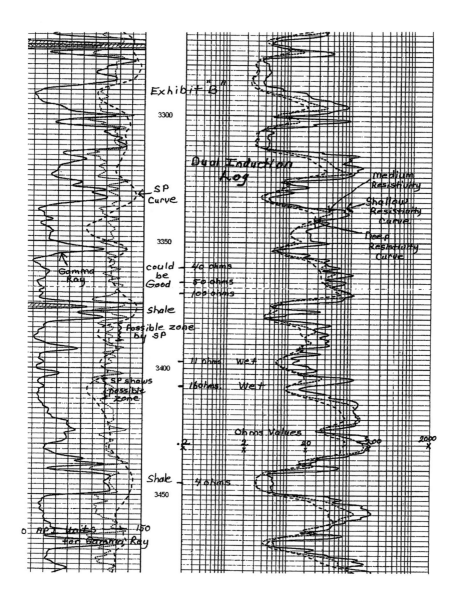

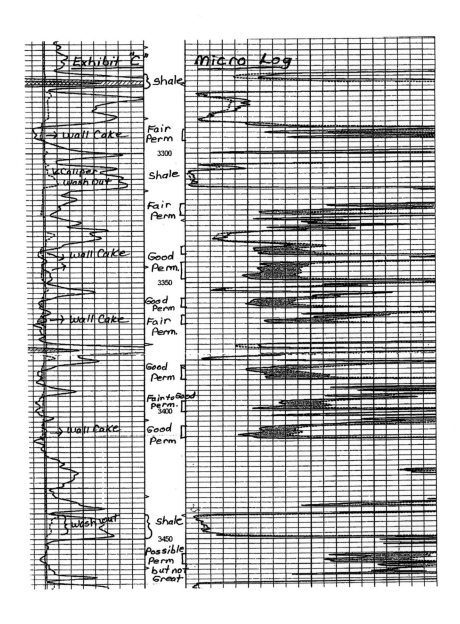

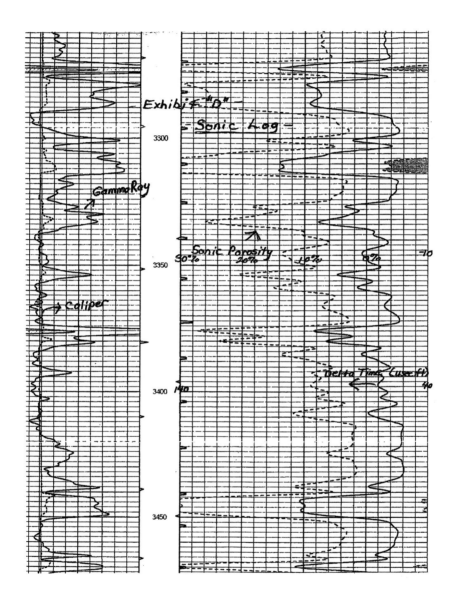

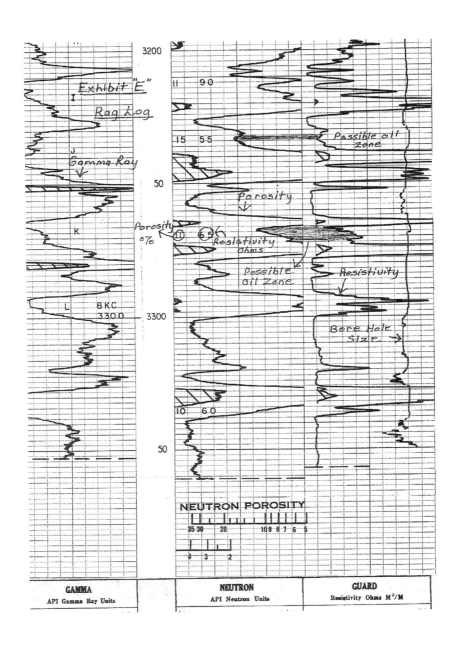

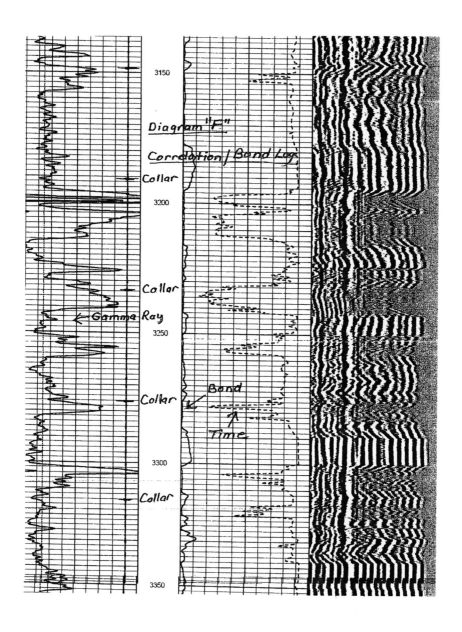

4

The Big Decision

You now have the well drilled, and it is time to make the big decision. You have spent a lot of money, but you are about to spend just as much as you have spent to see the bottom of the hole. What is involved in making this decision? As mentioned earlier, it will take about six thousand barrels to pay this well off once it has been put on production. However, you don't want to just break even. You want to make some real money. How do you go about making this decision?

You have a set of logs in your hand, and you know the results of your DSTs on the well. Attached, you will find three different logs that are labeled exhibit A and three labeled exhibit B. These are all logs from the same well. The first thing you need to do is mark the DSTs on the log where they would be and write out the results. On this particular well there were four DSTs run. I have marked them on the log. Next, I would go through the geologist report and mark down the shows of oil and odors plus any other descriptions that might help from the geo report. You will notice I have done that with both exhibits A and B.

Now, take a look at all three of the logs on the well. First of all, I go through the micro log, which is my favorite log. This log tells you whether you have permeability or not. You have marked the DSTs on the side. More than likely, you have more than one zone in your DST. Check out the recovery and the perm. Mark the zones with perm on each of the logs, the dual induction and the neutron/density log. Next I look at the neutron/density log and check the porosity. Does the porosity match up with the perm? Also, depending whether the DST recovered gas, I look for anything that looks like it might be trying to cross over on the log. When the density porosity tries to cross over the neutron porosity, this means you could have some gas. This is called the gas effect on a porosity log. This could really help you out if you have some gas on the test and you tested two or three zones together. Finally, I look at the dual induction log, and depending on the results of the test, I try to see what looks like it should be oil and what looks wet (watery). Now, putting all three logs together and the DSTs, I should be able to pick what is good and what is not.

Take at look at the results of DST 1. The recovery was 125' GIP, 55' oil cut mud (8% oil), 65' slightly oil cut watery mud (3% oil, 47% water), and 180' water. This is not a very good test. I would then look at the logs and see if I thought there was any possibility of this producing. The bottom-hole pressure was 449# to 441#. This test covered the A and part of the C. Notice that the lower part of the C, which was not in the test, looks wet. The upper part of the C looks fair, but there is no way to keep them separate, so I don't think this has much hope. Now I would look at the A, and usually you find the permeability in the upper part of the A. It is usually fractured porosity. In this particular case, it looks a little wet to me. Thus, I see nothing that looks good enough to be economical in this test. If this was all I had, I would have to plug the well. However, we tested three more times in this well. Take a look at DST 2. This test recovered 1,170' GIP, 365' gassy muddy oil (5% gas, 40% oil), 124' muddy gassy oil (20% gas, 70% oil), 186' clean oil (100% oil), and 124' gassy mud and water cut oil (20% gas, 45% oil, 20% water). The bottom-hole pressure was 776# to 763#. This is a nice little test. I can assure you that this will make an economical well. Now looking at the log, I notice that I have covered three zones, the D, E, and F. All three of the zones, looking at the micro log, have permeability. Looking at the compensated neutron/density log, the D and E appear to have some gas and the F does not. Now looking at the dual induction, the D zone looks fairly dry. By this I mean it looks like it will be all oil. Looking at the E, it looks like it will probably be oil, but the F looks wet. My first inclination is to leave the E alone because the F is fairly close. By close I mean it might have a good possibility of communicating (going together) on completion. Also, notice that the test had 20% water in the last description. I would say the water probably came out of the F zone, looking at the dual induction log. I would want to look at the bond log closely to determine this. I will probably perforate the D and see if I can make an all oil completion out of it. I will come back to the E after this zone has become uneconomical. This D zone looks like it could make 10,000 to 15,000 barrels pretty easily. Notice the flow pressures are very good also. Now take a look at DST 3. DST 3 recovered 450' GIP, 55' oil and gas cut mud (5% oil, 5% gas) and 60' heavy oil and gas cut mud (30% gas, 30% oil). This doesn't look like a real good test, but it could surprise you. DST 2 is not a normal test in the L-KC. This is much more normal. DST 2 recovered a lot of fluid and had great flow pressures. Now DST 3 has pretty good flow pressures too. This was a fairly long anchor test, which has some bearing on recovery. Provided I can find the right zone in this test, it would not surprise me at all to see 6 to 8 BOPH from this little test. This test covered the H through the L zones. As you will notice on the logs, every zone had a show and about the same kind of show. Now looking at the micro log, you have some perm in the L, K, J, and I. I really don't like the perm in the H. From here I go to the porosity log. The L has 10%; the K, 7%; the J, 9%; and the I, 10% porosity. Now looking at the dual induction, the L looks wet, the K looks like it might be wet, the J looks good, and maybe the I looks good. This gets really tough because the dual induction does not have enough time for the lines to move since the zones are very thin, only 2' each in the I, J, and K. The H looks good also on the dual induction. I would shy away from the L and K zones, but the other three look like definite possibilities. From these three tests, I would definitely have to run pipe. This is definitely a commercial well.

As you will notice, we ran one more DST, DST 4. This was a test that was run in the upper section of the Arbuckle, we would call reworked Arbuckle. It was not clean Arbuckle, as you can tell on the log. We had a few pieces of Arbuckle, along with cherts and sands. You will notice that the Arbuckle cleans up at about 3,628'. This is good, clean Arbuckle. We did not test it. However, we decided to give the Arbuckle a try from 3,628' to 3,632' when we completed the well. One thing important to remember, it is always nice to start at the bottom of the well and work yourself up the hole. This is not always the case, as the DSTs above may not be done that way, but usually it is nice to work up the hole. We opened the Arbuckle and dropped about 100 gallons of acid in the hole and treated lightly. We put this well on for 30 BOPD and about 70 BWPD. Basically, I tried this zone because it looks really good on the dual induction log. I felt like it was worth a shot. If I would have logged this well without the pipe setting tests from the L-KC, I would have definitely straddle tested this zone before I would have plugged the well. It looked that good.

I would be on location when they have the logs out of the hole. You have a pretty good idea from the DSTs what you want to do, but it is nice to have the log to look at and confirm what you feel about the well. You would make up a copy of the log just as I have done. The tops would be put on the logs for the Topeka through the Arbuckle. I would always have the subsea minuses on the log also. You want to see how close your geologist picks are. Usually they may be 2' to 3' off in one direction or the other. This was a very easy decision to make. I can guarantee you this will not always be the case. You will have to make tough decisions down the road. Hopefully, you can make the right ones.

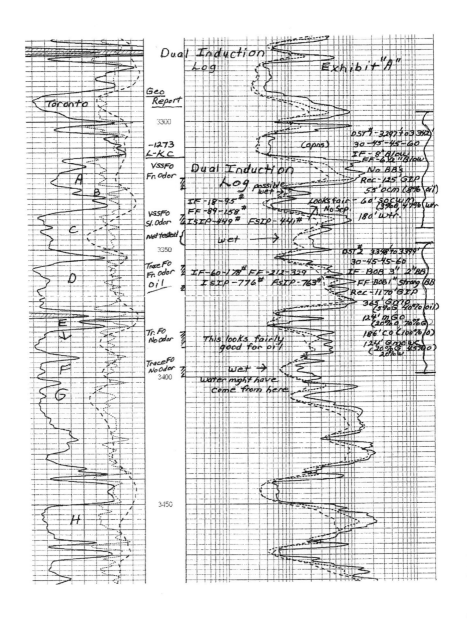

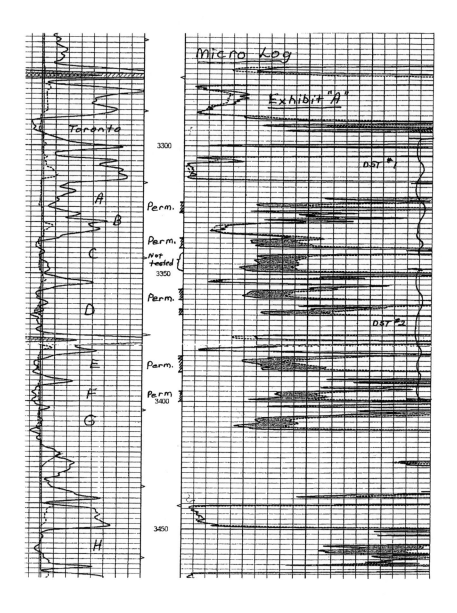

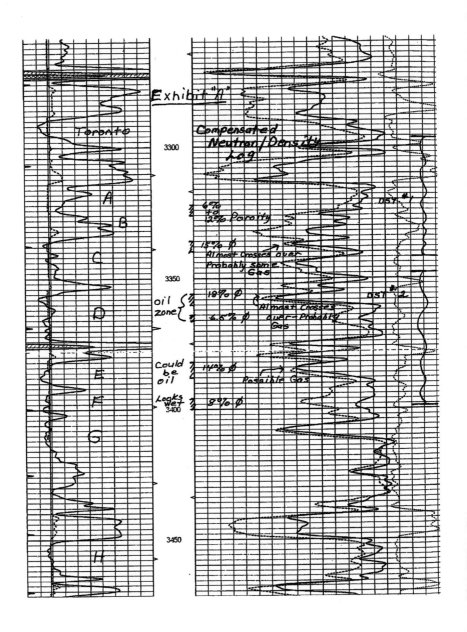

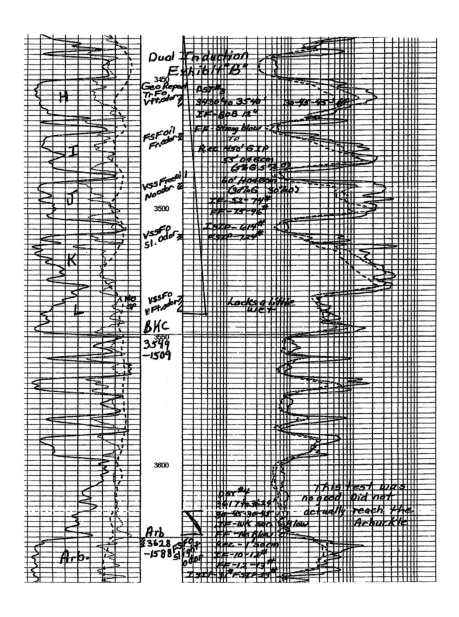

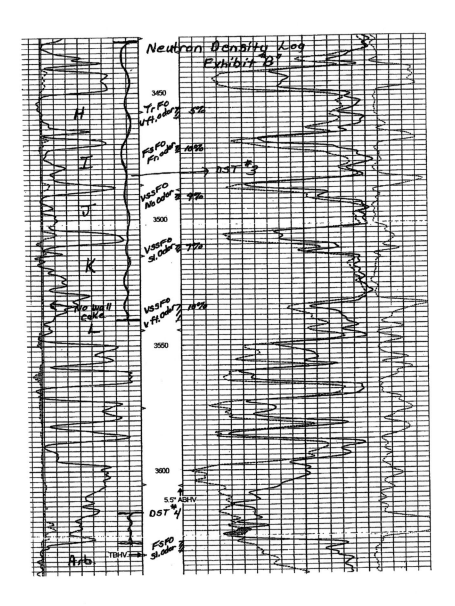

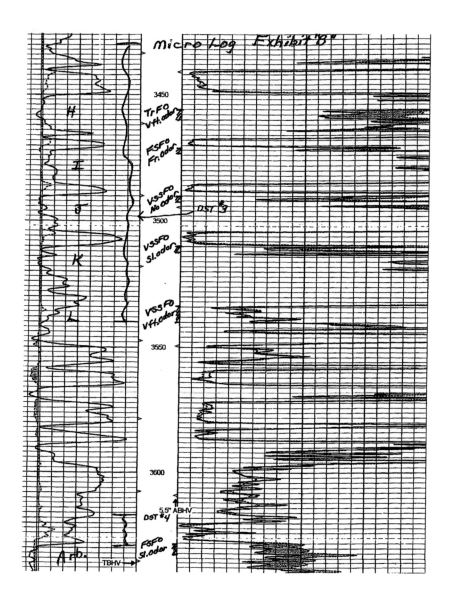

5

SETTING PIPE

You have drilled the well to rotary total depth (RTD), clear through the deepest possible producing zone. You have logged the well, and you have decided that you have something that will produce oil or gas. Now you are ready to run casing. You call the casing company and order a little more casing than your rotary TD. Order this threads off. This way if you have a problem with some of the joints, you will not have to wait. Make sure you have a little extra on hand.

You have ordered the casing, and it is now on location. It is racked up. First thing you need to do is look down every joint to make sure there is nothing in it like a rag, a rat's nest, or anything. Next you count the joints to make sure that you know exactly how many joints of casing are on this location. Next, number every joint on location with the first joint to be run as 1 and on down through every joint. Tally the joints threads off. Add up the pipe and get as close to the right amount as you can. The rig usually has what they call a landing joint, which is usually 8' to 11', depending on what the KB of the rig is. This makes it so that you can spot the top collar so it is just above ground level under the drilling floor. This way, the landing joint can just be backed out of the threads on the top collar instead of cutting off the top joint and welding what we call a slip collar on top. Years ago, before we began drilling through the Arbuckle, almost all top collars were cut off and welded because pipe was usually set on top of the Arbuckle, and it was very important that pipe be set in exactly the right spot. Thus, to do this, we cleaned out to bottom and made sure we were exactly on bottom, and we measured up from there and set the pipe, so most of the time, the top joint had to be cut off. Remember, when using a tape on, say, 90 to 100 joints, you could tally it 20 times and probably not get the exact same tally during any one of those times. The most accurate measurement when setting pipe was to go from RTD. In other words, we usually set so many feet off bottom. When you set in the top of the Arbuckle, we would call anything below the pipe, open hole. Most wells were completed in the top of the Arbuckle and drilled in. They were producing from the open hole. The last thing, dope all the threads and collars on the casing.

You have the pipe tallied, and you have any joints that you are not going to run marked out. In other words, you have written a big "Out" on those joints that you are not planning on running in this well. You now have to decide where you want to run centralizers, scratchers, baskets, and DV tools or port collars. Attached is a diagram A, which shows all this.

Centralizers are for centering the casing in the middle of the hole. Remember, you are running 4 1/2" or 5 1/2" casing in a 7 7/8" hole. You want your pipe as close to the middle of the hole as possible because you are going to cement this casing in place. You want to have cement all the way around the casing, not just on one side. Normally they are run on collars.

Scratchers are used through the zones of interest. I do not use scratchers, but some people do. The theory is that this will help clean up the wall cake (mud buildup) on the well bore through the zone, thus giving you a better bond to the well bore. There are two types of scratchers—rotating, in which the pipe is rotated once you get on bottom, or reciprocating, in which the pipe would be run up and down through the zone once you get on bottom. These are put on the outside of the casing. Once you get pipe on bottom, both of these would be done for a certain time while you are conditioning (circulating) the hole. You space the reciprocators so that when you raise and lower the pipe, you would overlap somewhat. I would always do it below the zone and above the zone at least 5'. This way you would probably be doing it across some of the shale above and below the zone, which will help you get a good bond when you cement the casing in place. I would only rotate and reciprocate the casing while you are conditioning the hole. Once you start cementing, I would shut this down. Some people don't do this. They rotate and reciprocate right through the cementing, but it looks like a good way to get your pipe stuck to me and not get back to bottom. I know this has happened before.

Baskets are run if you want to keep the hydrostatic pressure of the cement off a low pressure zone. In other words, if you have a low pressure zone that is permeable, it may not take much weight above it to break it down and you could easily lose circulation. This basket is a V-shaped canvas with metal fingers that expand out to the edges of the borehole, thus holding up the cement that passes by it. In other words, if a zone begins to break down, it would stop the cement from falling past this basket. Also, when you use a DV tool or port collar, you will normally run a basket below them to help stop the cement from going down.

DV tools and port collars are run in wells to cement a specific area of the pipe. The pipe will not be cemented from top to bottom. On bottom, the cement will only be brought up a few hundred feet above the highest pay zone (possible producing zone). Just for instance, in Kansas you are required to protect the freshwater systems in the area from becoming contaminated. To do this, the Kansas Corporation Commission requires you to cement the upper sections of the pipe. Thus, a DV tool or port collar is usually run from 800' to 2,000' depending on where the anhydrite is located in this area. The anhydrite, as mentioned before, is a hard section about 40' thick, located below the Dakota sand, which carries salt water in the bottom and freshwater in the upper section. The purpose of this cementing is to keep these separated from each other. Also, below the Dakota is a sand we call the Cedar Hills, which can be used as a disposal zone in certain areas. It lies above the anhydrite about 100'. I usually run a DV tool or port collar right above the anhydrite, and a basket right below it, in the anhydrite. This serves as protection for me and for the state. The Dakota zone is like a river in places, and can cut holes in your pipe in as little as 6 months in some areas. With the cement, you have some good protection from this eating through your casing. The DV tool and port collar are both for the same purpose. The difference between the two are as follows: The DV tool is cemented in place at the time that casing is set on the well. The port collar is done either before the well is completed, or after the well is completed. The DV tool will have to be drilled out before the well is completed. The port collar does not have to be drilled out before completion. It will be cemented when the tool is opened, which can be either before completion, or after completion.

Now we have the pipe tallied and you have marked the zones of interest on the log. From here, I calculate where all the collars will come out in reference to where I will be setting pipe on bottom. I mark where the centralizers will come out on the log. Now I look for possible spots to put centralizers. I want a centralizer on the collar of the first joint off bottom, as long as it does not come out in my zone. As for the rest of the centralizers, I want at least one below and one above every zone of interest. It is important to find spots that are hard on the log, and not washed out. I can find this out by looking at the caliper on one of the logs. I would not put a centralizer in the shale right above or below the zone of interest, and definitely not right in the middle of the zone. I don't believe you can always get a good cement bond around these centralizers. The cement job will be the most important part of this whole process, so it is very important to get this right. You need a good cement job so that different zones do not communicate. Once I have decided where I want these centralizers, I mark the collar on each joint so that they can be installed as we run them in the hole.

Now I decide if I need a basket. I know that I need one below the port collar or DV tool. I now figure where I would install one of these tools in the string. As I mentioned, I set this right above the anhydrite, or in the very top. To calculate this, I locate the top and bottom of the anhydrite and I subtract this from the bottom point that I am going to set pipe. Some people do this from the top and they usually have very little idea where the tool is located when they get done. I like accuracy.

Say the anhydrite was 1,200' to 1,240'. You are going to set pipe at 3,000'. I subtract 1,200' and 1,240' from 3,000', and get 1,760' to 1,800' off bottom. I now add the joints from 1 to 48 and I come up with 1,820'. Remember, the first joints in the hole will be on bottom, not the top. I subtract 1,820' from 3,000' and I get 1,180'. I put the DV tool or port collar on the top collar on the 48th joint. The port collar or DV tool goes on top of a collar. I mark the 48th collar and write DV tool on it so that when we get to this joint, I will know to put it on. Also, I mark the other end of the joint with the word basket, so when we get here, the basket can be installed and it will be in the anhydrite. Notice I want this basket in a hard section, such as the anhydrite, so it can expand and not let the cement go down. Normally, the basket will slide the length of the joint, or it can be clamped off in an exact point on the joint. I really prefer this.

If you want to run scratchers, you mark your casing about 10' above and 10' below the zone of interest. These scratchers will be installed on the pipe as you run in the hole. If you install the scratchers 8' apart, you will need to raise and lower the pipe about 10' to make sure you are getting everything you want cleaned off.

You now have the tally done. You call the cementer and tell him how much cement you will need. This can be calculated by volume between the outside of the casing and the borehole. Usually bring about 50% extra, in case you have some wash outs. My rule of thumb is 5 1/2" casing and 7 7/8" hole, about 100 sacks for 500' fill up. 4 1/2" casing in 7 7/8" hole, about 300' for every 100 sacks. Make sure you bring an extra 30 sacks for the mousehole and rathole. They need to be plugged. Now for the type of cement you want to use. They have all sorts of additives that you can add to cement—calcium, flow-seal, plaster of paris–type agent, and so forth. There are different types of cement—common, 60/40 Poz mix, 50/50 Poz mix, and many others. Each company has their own blend. I prefer to use common, with 10% salt. This salt seems to work as a soaking agent and appears to make for a better bond in water-bearing areas. Next you tell them what you need for float equipment. You will need a guide shoe and some sort of float system, whether just a regular insert float or a float shoe. Tell them whether you want them to bring a port collar or DV tool, and the number of centralizers and baskets you need, along with scratchers. If you are going to run a DV tool, you will order the cement for the top stage. They will calculate this because they probably know the area better than you do. This will usually be 60/40 Poz, 6% gel, 1/4 flow-seal per sack. You will give them a time to be on location. The cementer needs to bring all the equipment by a certain time. They need to be there before you are going to be running pipe. The pusher can give you a pretty good idea what time that will be because he has done it so many times.

While you have been doing all this, the rig crew has set up a casing crew to be out on location to help them lay down the drill pipe and run the casing. You have conditioned the hole for 1 1/2 hours, depending on the depth of the well. They have pulled all the drill pipe out of the hole. They have taken out the drilling nipple that sets on top the 8 5/8" casing that you set early in the well process. This is where the cuttings come up and out into the pit. This is under the drilling table and floor at ground level. The 8 5/8" surface was set about 3' below ground level because it will never be recovered, producer or dry hole. After the drilling nipple has been taken off, the cellar is jetted and the 8 5/8" bradenhead is installed on the 8 5/8" casing. It has two outlets- 2"- with a bull plug in one side and nipple and valve in the other side. Once pipe is on bottom and cemented, the 5 1/2" or 4 1/2" slips will be set once the well has been cemented and the rig is ready to start tearing down. Once this has been done, the rig will be released. This bradenhead is usually ordered with the casing, so that it comes out with it.

You are now ready to run pipe. The first joint is picked up. This can be a short joint, but if you are working close to bottom, I would suggest running at long joint. This will be called the shoe joint. On the thread end of this joint, the very bottom of the string, a guide shoe is screwed on. This is a cone shaped piece with a hole in the bottom all the way through the inside, about .8 of a foot long. It helps to guide the pipe down the hole. This guide shoe, if it is float shoe, will have a cage and seat so that the pipe will fill up as the casing is run in the hole. Once pipe is almost on bottom, the cementer will drop a weighted ball that will be pushed into this cage during circulation and will serve as a stop from letting fluid come back once cement is pumped to bottom.

In other words, this ball will seat up against the seat in the cage and not allow fluid to flow back up the casing, once cement has been pumped to bottom. The first joint is then put in the hole. On the inside of the collar of the first joint you will screw in a latch-down plug assembly. The latch-down plug assembly has a plastic ring that will latch on to the plug, once it has been pumped behind the cement to bottom. The nice thing about the latch-down plug is you have a double system for stopping the fluid from coming back, once the plug has been pumped to bottom. You have the ball that will be dropped before you break circulation that will go into the cage, and you have the latch-down plug itself to stop fluid from coming back. This gives you double the protection from things leaking back. The latch-down plug assembly is screwed into the inside of the collar and the next joint is screwed into the shoe joint. This bottom joint, as I mentioned, will be called the shoe joint. Where the latch-down plug is located, this will be the bottom of the hole, unless you drill it out. When the job is complete, this joint will remain full of cement. If a regular guide shoe is run on bottom, a guide shoe with no cage or seat, you can run an insert in the collar of the shoe joint instead of the latch-down plug assembly. There are two types of insert floats, one with a flapper and plastic insert that will allow the pipe to fill up as you are running casing, or one with a cage and seat, just like the float shoe. Diagram A also shows this type of system. If you are running an insert float in the top collar on the shoe joint, this is where the plug will stop. However, the plug will not have any latch down. You only have one system to stop fluid from coming back, once you have pumped the plug to bottom. This shoe joint will remain filled with cement unless you chose to drill it out. Let me explain why I mentioned the joint length of the first joint. If you are working close to bottom, I would not run a short joint on bottom because it is very easy to get water past your plug as you are pumping it down the hole. If this happens, you get contaminated cement, which will never set up correctly. With a long shoe joint, say 42'+ (5 1/2" casing), this gives you 1 barrel of space before it goes out and around the bottom of the pipe. With a short joint you only get about 1/3 of a barrel for bad cement, so it is very easy to get contaminated cement up around your casing and zone if you use a short shoe joint. This would not be good if it came up to the zone you are interested in. It would probably mean a bad cement job and a squeeze. The shoe joint is now in the hole and you're ready to move on.

As we run each joint, keep a careful eye on the joints and install the hardware that you have marked on the casing. This is why you numbered the casing. You know exactly where everything goes. Make sure you install the DV or port collar where it goes. I always carry a sheet of paper with me that tells me which joints need hardware and what. Also, I have figured the pipe on a sheet of paper. Total number of joints, total tally of those joints, length of the shoe (.8'), Length of the port collar or D V tool (usually 2.5' long), and the landing joint, if used. This is the total tally of all the pipe that will be run. Now I take the length of the first joint (shoe joint) and add the shoe (.8') on to it. This is the length of my shoe joint. I now subtract the shoe joint from my total pipe and this is where the plug will land when the cement has been displaced. Give a copy of this to the cementer so that he can figure the volume needed to displace the plug to the top of the float. I also give him a list of everything that goes on the pipe by number of joints, since he is the man installing them.

As we get to the top, with about 8 joints left, the cementer will drop a small metal weighted ball that will float down to bottom. Once we start circulating the hole, depending on what type of float we have, it will either knock out the plastic insert or go into the cage. You will be able to see this by the pump pressure while circulating. You should know exactly where the casing should land on the last joint, provided, everything has been tallied correctly. This depends on the rig you have used. Thus, you go up and tell the driller to slow down the last 4 or 5 joints and tell him where you think it should hit bottom. You should always tag bottom, no matter how far you plan on setting pipe off bottom. Since you more than likely have enough rathole made, it is not that important that this bottom be washed out, but it will give you a good idea that your tally was right and you did not make a mistake. After tagging bottom, you can install the landing joint, by backing the last joint out and locating your collar under the floor a little above ground level. Once you have this spotted, you can set the slips in the table and you have pipe set where you want it. Hopefully you have made enough rathole that you will not have to drill out the shoe joint. It's a lot cheaper to make a few extra feet of hole with the drilling rig than it is to drill out the shoe joint later. If you have run reciprocating scratchers, you would tie on to the casing with the mud pump and begin circulating (conditioning the hole) and raising the casing up and down for a certain period of time. If you have installed rotating scratchers, you would begin rotating the casing and circulating for a certain period of time. I would just tie on to the casing and condition the hole for about 20 to 30 minutes to get things moving off bottom and any mud we might have knocked off the walls on the way in, starting up the hole. This would be done with the rig mud pump. I have already seen the ball go through. I am now ready to get on with the job. I have pipe where I want it.

The cementers would now knock off the mud pump and tie their truck to the casing. I have mixed 500-gallon mud flush in their tanks. I pump this mud flush down the casing. This is to get the mud off the walls so it can be replaced by cement. It helps give you a better bond. Once this has been done, I follow it with cement, usually 150 to 200 sacks of common cement with 10% salt. Once all the cement has been mixed, they break off from the casing and wash out the pump and hoses. They release a rubber plug, which we call a wiper plug, and tie back on to the casing and pump water behind the plug to bottom. You count the number of barrels of water behind the plug. It is important that everything work correctly. You don't want to pump water past the end of the pipe. This is the most important part of the process. The cementing of the well will dictate the completion of the well, and how good it is. The volume has been calculated. Make sure you count the number of barrels pumped. When the plug lands, the pressure will come up to 1,200# to 1,500#. As you were pumping, once you started lifting the cement around the bottom of the casing, the pump pressure on the truck should be rising nice and slowly. The cement you are pumping weights 14lbs. to 15lbs. per gallon, so it is much heavier than the drilling mud. This is called the Lifting pressure, and depending on how much cement you are using, it should get up to 600# to 700#, right before the plug hits. Once you have the plug on bottom and it pressured up to 1,200#, let it set for a minute to make sure your casing is good. You then release the pressure slowly. If it dries up, your insert float, or float system has worked correctly. Check again to make sure no fluid is coming back. If the fluid does come back at you, you'll have to leave the pressure on the casing for 8 to 12 hours to let the cement set up.

Now we'll say that you have run a DV tool in this string. If all goes well on the bottom stage, the cementer will disconnect from the casing and drop the bomb that opens the DV tool. If a port collar was run, the job is done. Once the bomb has been dropped, you let it drift down to the DV tool. This will take 20 to 30 minutes, depending on how deep the tool was run. While you are waiting for the bomb to drop, the cementers are plugging the rathole and mousehole with the cement that will be used on the top stage. When they get done, they will hook back to the casing and pressure the casing to 1,000# to 1,500# and open the DV tool. The bomb moves a sleeve that will open two ports that will allow fluid to circulate around on the outside of the casing, from that point up to the surface. You will then establish circulation. Some people circulate the hole for a certain amount of time. I choose to start out mixing cement once we have good circulation. The amount of cement needed to circulate cement to the surface, has been calculated. You mix cement until the cement circulates to the surface. Once it circulates, and you have good cement to the surface, the cementers break off and wash up and drop another wiper plug (latch-down plug). This plug is displaced down to the DV tool with water and pressured to 1,400# to 1,600#, which closes the sleeve on the DV tool. Once again you release the pressure slowly. If it does not come back at you, the cement job is done. If it does come back, you'll have to leave pressure on it for at least 8 hours and the job is complete. The well will be left alone for 7 to 10 days, unless a port collar was used. The port collar does exactly the same thing as the DV tool. The difference is, this will be done when you complete the well. You run the port collar on the casing just like the DV tool, but you'll have to run tubing and a port collar opener to do this job. I'll explain this when we get to completions. Now, all we have to do before we start completing the well is to wait on cement (WOC).

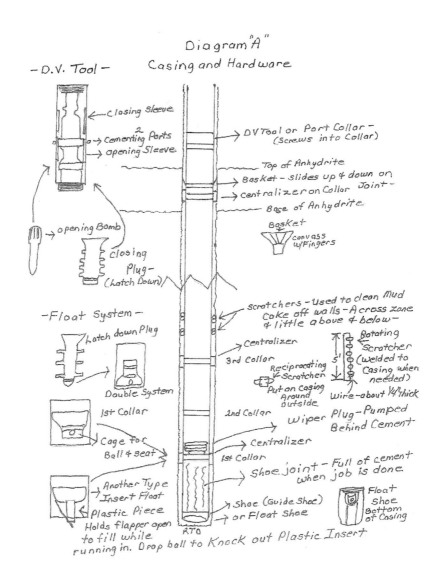

Diagram "A"
Casing and Hardware

- D.V. Tool -

- closing Sleeve
- 2 Cementing Ports
- opening Sleeve
- opening Bomb
- closing Plug - (Latch Down)

DV Tool or Port Collar - (Screws into Collar)
Top of Anhydrite
Basket - slides up & down on
Centralizer on Collar Joint -
Base of Anhydrite
Basket
canvass w/Fingers

-Float System-

Latch down Plug
Double System
1st Collar
Cage for Ball & Seat
Another Type Insert Float
Plastic Piece Holds flapper open to fill while running in. Drop ball to Knock out Plastic Insert
RTO

scratchers - used to clean mud Cake off walls - Across zone & little above & below-
Centralizer
3rd Collar
Reciprocating Scratcher
Put on casing Around outside
2nd Collar
Centralizer
1st Collar
Shoe joint - Full of cement when job is done
Shoe (Guide Shoe) or Float Shoe

Rotating Scratcher (welded to Casing when needed)
5'
Wire-about ¼" thick
Wiper Plug - Pumped Behind Cement
Float Shoe Bottom of Casing

6

COMPLETION OF THE NEW WELL

You have pipe set and the cement has cured. Diagram A is how everything looks with the casing set and ready to go. You're now ready to start the completion. If a port collar was run in this well, you could have already ran the cased hole correlation/bond log off of a portable mast. With a port collar, you can get to the bottom of the hole. With a DV tool, it will have to be drilled out before you can run the cased hole log.

The best time to do the port collar is before you have done anything else. All you have to do is run the port collar opener on tubing and locate the port collar. The hole must be full. Once you have found it, you pressure up on the casing to 800# to 1,000# to make sure your casing is good. You then open the port collar by turning the tubing to the left, usually about a quarter of a turn. Once the port collar has been opened, and the pump truck is tied to the casing, you begin pumping slowly and you should feel a blow out the hoses coming off the 8 5/8" casing.. Take the hose from the casing and hook it to the tubing and begin mixing cement. The cement would be the same as what you would use for a D. V. Tool. While you are mixing cement, you should get fluid coming out the hoses on the 8 5/8" casing after a short time. You mix cement until you have cement coming out the hoses. Once you have good cement to the top, you displace the cement in the tubing down to about 100' above the bottom of the tubing. You then disconnect from the tubing and relocate the port collar and close the port collar by turning the tubing to the right. Once you have it closed, you repressure the casing to 800# to 1,000# to make sure it is closed and holding. Now you run about 5 joints of tubing below the port collar and circulate the excess cement out of the hole and clean it up. Pull the tubing and opener, and we are ready to go to the next step. With a port collar in the hole, you can do this after you have completed the well. This is really handy if you are not sure that you have a well worth putting on. If the port collar is not done after completion, in other words, if the well is not worth putting on, then you can back off the casing above the cement on the bottom stage and pull it out of the hole and reuse it. This is a great advantage. The only difference, if you do go ahead and do the port collar after completion, you will have to run a retrievable bridge plug into the top of the cement above your zones, as a plug, and open the port collar just like before.

If a DV tool was run, you will have to run a 4 7/8" bit for 5 1/2" casing, or a 3 7/8" bit for 4 1/2" casing. Depending on the depth and size of tubing to be used, you may need drill collars for some weight, to drill out the DV tool. Go ahead and drill it out and make sure that you ream it good so that you can get tools through it without any problem. Depending whether you have enough rathole below your first joint, you may have to clean it out clear down to the float. Hopefully, you had plenty of room. If so, pull the tubing and bit and run the cased hole log without cleaning out clear to TD.

For a cased hole log, I would recommend that you run a correlation/bond log. Diagram F, in the logging chapter, is a partial picture of a correlation/bond log. This has a Gamma log, which shows you the formations. You will use this to tie the open hole log into the cased hole log so that all depths will be the same. Most loggers are smart enough to do this, but you definitely need to make sure this is done. It will have a bond log curve, which is done with sound reflectors. From this you can tell how your cement is bonded to the pipe. About half the time, I'm not sure they are worth the paper they're written on, but I continue to run them. Also, you will have a collar log, which shows you where all the collars are located in relation to the pipe. This is what we will perforate off of, the location of each zone, relative to the collars. This will be logged from the bottom of the hole, which should be right above the float in the casing, which we now call the plug back total depth (PBTD), above the Topeka or at least the highest zone of interest. I usually run it all the way to the top of the cement, wherever that comes out.

Once we have the cased hole log run, and remember, the hole needs to be full of fluid for this log to be run correctly, we are ready to perforate. We swab the casing down with a casing swab, to about 400' or 500' above the zone to be perforated. This will serve as a buffer when the gun goes off. In other words, this will help to hold the gun in place when it goes off. Otherwise, it will have a tendency to jump up the hole or split the gun, which makes for an easy way to get hung in the hole. The perforating gun comes in all lengths and sizes. You have decided that the zone you are going to shoot, from the open hole log, is 3' thick. Thus, you want a gun 3' long. You can order any amount of holes you want, up to 6 per foot. I recommend 4 shots per foot. There are different kinds of charges that are put in the gun. I recommend using the largest charge they have, called expendables. These are usually 39 gram charges. They will penetrate about 39 inches into the well bore. Some people only use expendables in the Arbuckle, where they hope to get production natural. I prefer them for all shots. Penetration is important. The further you can get out into a zone the easier it will be to treat with acid. You now lower the gun into the hole on the wire line with a collar locator attached to the top of the gun. The center of the collar locator has been measured down to the top shot of the gun. This is usually 2' to 3'. This is called the standoff. You run the gun down on the wire line to the area that you want to perforate. You will pick out about 3 collars off the cased hole log in the area that you are planning on shooting the gun, either above or below, it really does not matter. You move about 5' below the first collar and start moving up slowly, watching the collar locator and stopping right in the middle of the collar. Now you change the footage on the line meter to correlate with the footage on the cased hole log collar. Go do the same thing with the other two collars that you have picked out, making adjustments as needed. Try to be as accurate as possible. Now you are ready to position the gun to perforate your zone. Remember, you want to shoot from 3,605' to 3,608'. You have a 3' gun in the hole and a 2.5' standoff (2.5' from the center of the collar locator down to the first shot). You would position the collar locator as follows:

	top shot	3,605.00'
−	standoff	2.50'
	collar locator	3,602.50'

You want the collar locator positioned at exactly 3,602.5'. Your top shot will be at 3,605' with the bottom shot being at 3,608'. Once the gun is in position, the power is switched to shooting position and the gun is fired. You now have holes from 3,605' to 3,608'. Some of the new trucks run a strip log across the area to be shot, with about 3 collars. You can then make a copy of the strip and set it right on top of your correlation/bond log and tie your collar locator right into the log. This is really nice and very accurate. Once you have the zone perforated, you have a decision to make, either run tubing and packer and swab down, or swab the casing down. In water-driven zones, such as the Arbuckle, I would recommend not swabbing the casing. Casing swabbing has a tendency to put too much vacuum on the formation, and thus, you can easily suck water into the well bore. We don't want this. For gas-driven zones such as Lansing-Kansas City, I really see no problem with casing swabbing. Either way, you swab the hole down and put it on a test and see what you have for fluid. Attached is diagram B, a view of what we call swabbing.

As I mentioned earlier, I believe I would prefer to run packer and tubing to swab any zone down. A packer is a tool that can Isolate a zone from the top side. For instance, say you shot a zone from 3,605' to 3,608'. You would run a packer on 2 7/8" tubing. I usually run in and leave the packer swinging first of all, at about 3,580', above the zone, or somewhere fairly close to the zone, where ever it comes out to the nearest joint with the tally. I would then run the tubing swab and make a pull and see what we have. Remember, good records should be kept on all that is done to the well. Records are important. This goes not only for the completion, but for the drilling, as well. Keep track of your fluid, the amount and percentage of oil. I usually decide what I have and then set the packer and make a pull off the seating nipple. From here, I usually make 15 minute pulls for 1 hour and then the 1 hour total is recorded in my records. Once you have determined what you have, you can make decisions on what you need to do from there. Let's say the well is swabbing 12 barrels of oil per hour(BOPH). We would call this Natural, since we have done nothing to the well except perforate. This is a good zone. You would swab this until you have it cleaned up, which means the oil is good and clean and there is no mud in it. If this was an Arbuckle zone (water-driven in most places), I would probably hang this well on just as it is. Swabbing 12 bbl per hour, this would probably make somewhere around 100 to 125 BOPD. If this was a Lansing-Kansas City zone, it probably would not clean up quite as easily. I would probably treat this with acid. Now there are several kinds of acid, mud acid (MA), nonemulsion (NE), intensified nonswelling (INS), and many others. The first thing that most people would use on this well, is mud acid. I would go in with 250 gallons 15% mud acid. I would release the packer and go down and position the bottom of the tubing, below the packer, right below the bottom of the perforations. We would run in with the swab and tag fluid. From here, you can figure what volume it will take to get the acid on bottom. By this I mean, you can drop a certain amount of fluid down the hole to get acid right on bottom. You still have the packer unset and you have lowered it so that the bottom of the packer is right below your lowest perforation. You know where the bottom of your tubing is and you have tagged fluid. By using the chart in exhibit C, you can figure out how much fluid it would take to get acid on bottom. You subtract the fluid level from the bottom of the tubing. This will give you the amount of fluid that you have in the hole. From here, you find the number on the chart that is the way your hole is configured. By this I mean, you have 2 3/8" tubing and 5 1/2" casing, or 2 7/8" tubing and 5 1/2" casing, or 2 3/8" tubing and 4 1/2" casing, or so forth. Make sure you get the right multiplier for the particular size equipment you have in the hole. The fluid amount will be multiplied by the per foot amount in barrels that would need to be dropped down the tubing to get acid right on bottom. Always go over this amount at least 1/2 to 1 bbl. It is vitally important that you get acid on bottom. Once you set the packer, it's tough to get it on bottom if it loads early. Now you drop the acid and you need to give it some time to get down there. It will take a little while depending on depth. Once it is down there, you pull the packer up and set it. By setting it, I mean you turn the tubing to the left or right, depending on what kind of packer you have in the hole. This packer has a set of slips and a J slot that pulls up against a rubber and sets against the walls of the casing. This rubber stops anything from going by. There are set-down packers and tension packers and they both work basically the same way, but the slips are in different positions. You now have the zone isolated from the packer on down. You don't need anything below you because you have the float as bottom. Attached is diagram D, a diagram of an isolated zone. This is a simple one zone completion. Once the packer is set, the tubing is loaded, keeping track of how many barrels it takes to load. You have figured the volume of the tubing and casing under the packer that it would take for acid to be on bottom. When it loads you see what it took in relation to what you figured. If it took more, it loaded late. If it took less, you loaded early. I get a little upset when it loads early.

Now you have acid on bottom. You wish it would go on its own. Don't forget, you have a lot of hydrostatic pressure on it, just with the hole loaded. Usually it does not go on its own. The type of job we are doing here, is called a breakdown job. We are trying to get into the zone. If this zone is making 12 BOPH, it might go on its own. Usually you are not that lucky. Often the zone is giving up nothing. The mud and cement that has been used in the drilling and setting of pipe, has blocked the zone off. More than likely it is going to take some pressure to get into this zone. Start out as slowly as you can and work your way up. Acid will eat on limestone at a fairly rapid rate. It eats on dolomite much slower. Most people have the idea that acid eats on cement. This is definitely not the case. It might etch it, but it will not eat on it. This is why it often takes a fair amount of pressure to get to the zone. Always remember, the reason for using cement is to keep one zone isolated, or separate from another. You want to get this acid into the formation as easily as possible, by this I mean at the lowest pressure possible. You do not want to communicate to another zone. This is where experience comes into play. Knowing the area helps, along with the use of the bond log. It can give you some idea of how much pressure you can put on a formation before it will communicate. However, that said, I have seen good bond go easily, and bad-looking bond hold quite well. That's why I said I am not sure why I run bond logs because I have seen them not necessarily tell the truth. This 250 gallons of acid is strictly for breakdown. This is just to get a start at cleaning up the well bore. Actually, this is all the acid is for. Depending on how many feet of perforations you have, this will depend how much acid you will want to use after the breakdown. On the breakdown, as I mentioned, you want to get the acid into the formation at the lowest pressure possible. Usually you will begin by stagging the acid in at whatever pressure you can. Hopefully it is a low pressure. Once you have stagged in about a 1 barrel of acid, and while getting this barrel into the formation, it will get faster and faster, to a point where you can pump on it steady. Once you start pumping on it steady, it will usually break back, this is called the breakdown. Usually you will find a rate, say 0.25 to 0.5 bpm at a certain pressure. I usually go a barrel or two over the tubing volume to make sure all the acid is displaced. This all needs to be written down and kept in your completion report. You will record the last pressure reading and the pumping volume. Once you have shut down, you record this as the instant shut-in pressure (ISIP). I usually let it set for 15 minutes and record every 5 minute pressure till the well goes on a vacuum. Most good zones will go on a vacuum in 2 to 5 minutes. However, not all areas are the same, so this is not true everywhere.

Once the well has been treated with the mud acid and you have waited the 15 minutes, you begin swabbing the well down and putting on a test. I write down where the initial swab tagged fluid and we know how much fluid we put in when we treated. This is called the load. We swab the well down through the tubing. I usually make two pulls off the seating nipple (This is a 1.1' sub that is a little bit smaller than the tubing on the inside so the mandrel on the bottom of the swab bar will not go out the end of the tubing) and we call this the swab down. As an example, let's say we treated with 6 bbl of acid, and the tubing and casing volume below the packer was 15.3 bbl. We overflushed it 2 bbl. The total load would be 23.3 bbl. The well went on a vacuum in 3 minutes. After letting set 15 minutes, we ran in and fluid was at 1,000' from the surface. We swabbed the well down and made two pulls off the seating nipple and the total fluid we recovered was 18.5 bbl. This would mean we were 4.8 bbl short of getting our load back. All of this would be on your report. Now you put the well on 15 minute pulls. The pulling unit crew will gauge the test tank in 1 hour, after making 4 pulls. They have been catching a small sample bucket full of the fluid on each pull. They drain the bucket and calculate the percentage of oil. We then take an average for the hour on the percentage and gauge the tank. Let's say they have 5 bbl in the hour at 35% oil. You are 0.2 bbl over your initial load and you are getting some oil. This is good. You can test this as long as you like. I would probably test it another hour or two, until it stabilizes. Remember, every hour cost money and you don't make any money off this well until it goes to a stock tank and it is sold. Time is money in this business. Also, when I say 15 minute pulls, I do not mean wait on the top of the ground until 15 minutes is up. This will turn into 1 1/2 hours if you do it that way. The 15 minutes mean you come off the seating nipple, or bottom if you have more fluid than you can handle to get to the seating nipple. This is a real 1 hour test. From these tests, you can get some idea what the well will make. Usually, it will be 25% to 35% of what you are swabbing, if you are pulling from the seating nipple. If you cannot get it swabbed down to bottom, then it is anyone's guess what it might make.

You have tested the well for a couple of hours and it has not completely cleaned up, or it did not go on a vacuum as you thought it might. It may be that you only have a couple of barrels per hour, which is not enough fluid to produce much. You would probably want to retreat with a different kind of acid. In limestone I use what they call NE acid, which is non emulsifying acid. Sometimes oil will become emulsified, and this type of acid with help eliminate that. In dolomites, such as Arbuckle, I use INS acid, which is intensified nonswelling acid. Lots of times you have clays and shale in the Arbuckle that have a tendency to swell with acid. This type of acid helps to stop that kind of swelling. Usually I use 15% acid. You can get this up to 28% acid or down to whatever concentration you would like. Usually in sands, I use 7.5% at the most because acid really has nothing to eat on in a sand. With a higher concentration, you can easily frost the sand off to where you can't get into it or you can't get anything out of it. It kind of makes the sandstones weld together. You can get all sorts of chemical combinations, depending on what you think the zone might react to in a good way. Usually that is anyone's best guess. As I mentioned, I usually use certain kinds of acid for certain kinds of rocks. The next question is how much acid does a person use? Remember one thing, acid does not make oil. Basically, what you are trying to do with acid is clean up the well bore. Normally, this would not take much. Once in a while, when you are breaking a well down, you can tell whether you are pushing mud in front of you. When this happens, you should definitely retreat the well. The amount of acid has nothing to do with the amount of oil the well will make over the long haul. It does have an effect on how fast you might get it out. Personally, I do not see the purpose of 2,000 or 3,000 gallons of acid. If you can't get it with 500 gallons to 1,000 gallons, you probably won't. You can tell when a well has cleaned up. Depending on what you decide to retreat the well with, you hope you can get a steady rate and you can get the well to go on a vacuum. The rate you pump the acid into the well, is not as important as it is to get it into the zone. Also, depending how the well treats the second time, will depend on how much overflush you will give the acid. Overflush is the amount that you pump over the volume of acid that you pump out into the formation. In other words, overflush begins once you have pumped all the acid out into the formation. Say you pump the acid 10 barrels past the perforations plus the volume in the tubing and casing down to the perforations. This 10 barrel would be 10 barrel of overflush.

Once you have gotten the acid and overflush in the well, you would want to let it set for at least 30 minutes. More than likely, you will get a pretty good kick from a job this size. In other words, once you swab part of the load back, the swab hose is going to kick quite a bit. If you ever find yourself swabbing a well back after an acid job into a pit, make sure that the hose is tied down securely because it will kill you if it gets loose while it is kicking. You swab the well back, catching samples as you go. Once you have made a couple of pulls off the seating nipple, you can put the well on test.

Once you have tested the well, hopefully you have enough to put the well on production. From the DSTs that you ran during the drilling of the well, and the log evaluation, you should have a good idea whether you have what you thought you should have. From here you pull the tubing and packer and run the tubing, pump, and rods and get the well ready for production.

This is what we call a simple completion on a zone. Now let's say you have two or three zones in the Lansing-Kansas City that you want to open. There are a couple of ways that you can do this. First, you could shoot out the three zones that you want to open. When I say shoot out, I mean you shoot the whole zone out at say 4 shots per foot. Now, if you want to save money and time, you can shoot 1 hole in each of the three zones. We call this limited entry. Let me go into further detail on each of these.

First of all, shooting out the three zones. You go in with 3 different guns. Say the first zone is 2' thick, the second zone is 4' thick, and the third zone is 6' thick. You would go in with a gun the length of each zone. You will see this on the micro log, the permeability of each zone. You go in with one gun on each run, so it will take you three runs. I always start with the deepest zone and work my way up the hole. As you run each gun, you can check for any fill up by where you tag fluid on each gun. Some of the newer perforating companies have what they call select-fire, which means they can run two guns in the hole at the same time. They can shoot each gun separately, one at a time, by reversing the polarity of each gun that you shoot. Personally, I do not like this because I'm not convinced that the right gun is shot in the right spot each time, but it can be done. Once the zones have been shot out, you can run a bridge plug and packer on your tubing and isolate each one of the zones. Attached is diagram E, reflecting the isolation of a zone with a bridge plug and packer. You have looked at the bond log and determined that you think each zone is separate. By this I mean there is good cement bonding between each zone that you have shot out. The bridge plug is for isolating the bottom and the packer is to isolate the top. Thus, you run the bridge plug down below the zone that you plan on working over first and set the bridge plug. The bridge plug is set by torquing the tubing to the left on the new type plugs and then pulling tension into them. You then go back down and set on the plug and turn slightly to the right to get off the bridge plug. In other words, you have come completely off the bridge plug. It is setting in the casing all by itself. Now you come up above the zone and set the packer, by turning the tubing to the right and setting down on the packer. The slips on the packer go out against the walls of the casing with a rubber below, which is squeezed out against the casing. This is called a set-down packer, or a model R packer. You now have the zone isolated all by itself. Run the tubing swab and see if the well is making anything Natural. If not, you will release the packer and lower the bottom of the packer (the bottom will have a catcher that goes over the top of the bridge plug to set and release the bridge plug) below the bottom perforation and tag fluid and spot acid just like we did before. Once you have spotted the acid you pull up above the zone and reset the packer and treat the well. As before, you want to treat the zone as lightly as possible because you want the acid to stay in the zone and not communicate to the other zones that you have opened. You ask what keeps the zones from becoming communicated? The cement that you put in the well when you ran casing. That is why the running of pipe and cementing of casing is so important. It is vital that each zone be separate. If not, you may never get into the zone that actually produces the oil. In other words, you might have spent a lot of money drilling and testing the well, and never end up with what you should have had if you could have broken down the right zone and not communicated. Once you have treated and tested the first zone, you go down and release the packer and go down and get hold of the bridge plug and release the bridge plug. You pull it up and set the bridge plug below the next zone and pull the packer up and set the packer above the next zone and you have it isolated. You go through the same process as before. When it has been completed, you release the packer and go down after the bridge plug and move up over the top zone and do the same thing.

Now, what if you did communicate from one zone to the other? How would you know if you communicated? On the lower two zones, once you set the packer, you want to keep a close eye on the backside, the 2" valve on the 5 1/2" or 4 1/2" tubing head. It will usually have two openings, one with a bull plug and the other with a nipple and valve. Make sure the valve is open and put a rag over the end. If the rag sucks in when you make a pull off bottom with the swab, more than likely the zones are communicated. You may want to make two or three pulls just to make sure. It should suck every time. Thus, the zones are communicated. Now for the top zone, this is much more difficult to tell whether it is communicated to the lower zones. You need to keep close track of the amount of fluid and the type and percentage of fluid so that you will have some idea if it is about what you had from below. One thing that I always do when working on more than one zone at a time, is break each zone down lightly at first before I ever retreat a zone. In other words, I set over each zone separately and treat them with 250 gallons of 15% mud acid and treat them as lightly as possible before I ever retreat a zone. More than likely, if you do communicate, it will be on the retreat. This way I have a lot better chance of staying in each zone, and they all get broke down before I put pressure on them when I retreat. In other words, I believe it is more important to get each zone broke down than to retreat. Too many times I have seen people treat a zone and retreat a zone and communicate up to the next zone before ever breaking it down. How do you ever know that you got into the next zone up? You don't.

What could you do if you do communicate? There are several possibilities. First of all, you could squeeze all the zones off and start over. What do I mean by squeeze? You would pull the tubing, packer, and bridge plug out of the hole. You then run down with a packer on the bottom of your tubing. Set about 100' above the top zone and set the packer. Load the backside with water and pressure up to 500 and shut it in. Now hook to the tubing and take an injection rate. Once you have an injection rate, you can probably get some idea of how much cement you will be able to get into the formations. You begin mixing cement and pump the cement into the zones. Let's say you mix 150 sacks common cement. Once you get the cement mixed, you will break off and clean out the pump and lines. Now you tie back on to the tubing. You know exactly how much fluid (water) it will take to displace all the cement past the end of the packer. You also know how much fluid it takes to fill from the top perforation up to the packer. You will displace the cement down the tubing and below the packer. You know exactly what the volume is to get all the cement out of the tubing. You would go 1/4 to 1/2 bbl past the end of the tubing. Hopefully, by the time you get this to bottom, you will have about 500# to 1,000# on the pump. You will have lowered your rate (slowed down). At this point you shut down and start letting the cement set up. This may take a couple of hours. You will move the pump every once in a while and start squeezing on the cement. The harder the cement gets, the faster it will pressure up. You will squeeze it to 1,500#. As you are squeezing the cement, you are dehydrating it, squeezing the water out of it. The cement used in oil production is not like the cement for your drive way. It is straight common cement, with no sand. You want to always know where you are as far as volume pumped and how much it takes to get to the end of your tubing and how much the volume is that will get you past the perforations. You do not want to go past your perforations or you will be starting all over again. The zone has taken all of your cement. That is why you set the packer 100' above the top zone, so you have about 2.5 bbl of cement to play within the casing below the packer. If you are squeezing and you want to displace the cement down to bottom and leave some cement in the tubing, you really need to be careful and move the cement more often in the squeezing process. You do not want to leave cement inside the tubing and packer or you will be stuck! Some zones, such as Arbuckle, will squeeze on the run. Say you mixed 50 sacks common cement and your displacement to bottom was 15 bbl. About the time you get 10 bbl of displacement out, your pressure is already at 1,500#. You have squeezed it on the run. Once you have gotten to the 1,500# mark and you think it is solid, you will release the pressure and make sure it does not come back at you. Now you release the packer and circulate the hole clean. Once you have this done, I would pull the packer and wait on cement. This cement will have to be drilled out. Most of the time, about 12 hours of curing time is enough. Some people will release the packer and wash out the cement in the casing and hope that the squeeze holds, but I would not recommend that. Once you have the cement drilled out and cleaned up to bottom, you are ready to start over, hoping that the cement has replaced the void areas between the zones. Basically you do exactly the same process as before, as far as completion is concerned.

Another thing you can do is what we call a rock salt job. Say you have three zones that are all communicated. More than likely, you can treat these three zones at a fairly high rate per minute with a very low pressure. You would set over all three of the zones and give them say 1,500 gallons of acid at say 3 bpm at 500#. More than likely you do not have all the zones broke down. You may just have one or possibly two broke down. This is where rock salt comes in handy. You try to decide how much it would take to fill the zone that you think is broke down with rock salt. The rock salt is going to go to the zone with the least resistance. Since the zone is already open, I would probably start with 250# of rock salt (This 250# is mixed with water so it can be pumped down the tubing) and pump this down the tubing. Again, you know the displacement volume to get this rock salt to the perforations. You are always keeping track of the number of barrels that you pump, no matter what kind of job you are doing. Right behind the rock salt, I would pump 500 gallons of acid (500 gallons is equal to 12 barrels). As you are pumping, you are watching the pressure gauge. When the rock salt hits the perforations, you will start to see a pressure increase. You are pumping at 3 to 7 bpm, depending on what kind of pressure you have on the well head. You want it to pressure up so that when the acid hits the bottom of the tubing, the rock salt has blocked off the first zone that was broken down and this new acid will go into one of the other two zones. Usually you can see this breakdown when the pressure drops off somewhat. Since you have a third zone, you may want to follow with another 250# of rock salt to plug off this second zone and then another 500 gallons of acid so that you can break down the third zone. You would be amazed how well this can work in the right conditions. One thing for sure, you do not want any high water-bearing zones above or below you because you may have quite a bit of pressure on the well head and you could easily communicate to them. This is basically a hope-and-pray method. You have very little control of anything. I like to have some control, even if it's only in my mind. You might ask, what happens to the rock salt? It will dissolve over time and with fluid movement. As you swab the well down, the salt will dissolve and come back as salt water.

Now for the limited entry method of completing a two or three zone well. The whole theory of limited entry, is that the holes that you perforate are all exactly 3/8" in diameter. You can only put so much liquid through a 3/8" hole at one time. We in the oil industry, say this amount is 2.5 barrel per minute. So, if you have 2 zones you shoot 1 hole in each zone, and you pump a liquid at 5 bpm, then both holes or zones should be getting treated or broke down. Thus, if you have 3 zones, you shoot 1 hole in each zone, and you pump 7.5 bpm, all three zones should be getting treated or broke down. There was a time when I thought this might be the way to go. However, over the years, I have been back in on some of these limited entry wells and found out that some of the zones were never treated. I did this be isolating the zones by themselves. I would not recommend completing wells in this fashion. I know that it is still being done. This is another instance of having very little control over the situation. When you isolate one zone at a time, you do have some control, as long as you can keep the zone from communicating.

The best way to complete wells is one zone at a time. This way, hopefully each zone will be maximized to its fullest potential. After all, isn't that what you want?

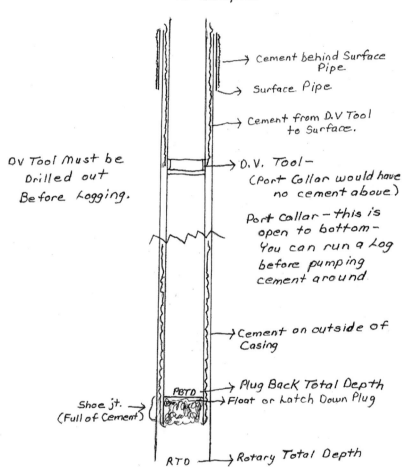

Diagram "A"
Casing Set & Ready
to Complete

Cement behind Surface
Pipe

Surface Pipe

Cement from D.V Tool
to Surface.

Ov Tool must be
Drilled out
Before Logging.

D.V. Tool —
(Port Collar would have
no cement above)

Port Collar — this is
open to bottom —
You can run a Log
before pumping
cement around.

Cement on outside of
Casing

PBTD → Plug Back Total Depth
→ Float or Latch Down Plug

Shoe jt. →
(Full of Cement)

RTD ——→ Rotary Total Depth

Diagram "B"

Casing Swab

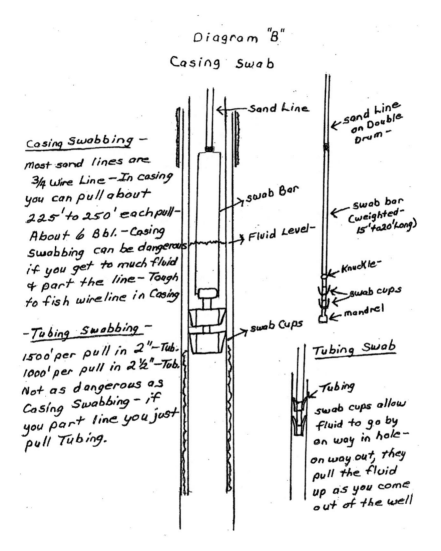

Casing Swabbing —

Most sand lines are
3/4 Wire Line — In casing
you can pull about
225' to 250' each pull —
About 6 Bbl. — Casing
Swabbing can be dangerous
if you get to much fluid
& part the line — Tough
to fish wireline in Casing

— Tubing Swabbing —
1500' per pull in 2" — Tub.
1000' per pull in 2½" — Tub.
Not as dangerous as
Casing Swabbing — if
you part line you just
pull Tubing.

Sand Line

Sand Line
on Double
Drum —

Swab Bar

swab bar
(weighted —
15' to 20' Long)

Fluid Level —

Knuckle —

swab cups

mandrel

swab Cups

Tubing Swab

Tubing

swab cups allow
fluid to go by
on way in hole —
on way out, they
pull the fluid
up as you come
out of the well

97

Exhibit "C"
Volumes

ALLIED
CEMENTING CO., LLC
Cementing & Acidizing Services

Tubing Size and Capacity

Size	Weight (lb/ft)	ID	bbl/ft
1.9	2.9	1.61	0.0025
2.063	3.25	1.751	0.003
2.375	4.7	1.995	0.0039
2.875	6.4	2.441	0.0058
3.5	9.3	2.992	0.0087

Casing Size and Capacity

Size	Weight (lb/ft)	ID	bbl/ft
4 1/2"	9.5	4.09	0.0163
4 1/2"	10.5	4.052	0.0159
4 1/2"	11.6	4	0.0155
5 1/2"	14	5.012	0.0244
5 1/2"	15.5	4.974	0.0238
5 1/2"	17	4.892	0.0232
7"	20	6.331	0.0405
7"	23	6.366	0.0394
7 5/8"	29.7	6.875	0.0459
8 5/8"	24	8.097	0.0637
9 5/8"	47	8.681	0.0732
13 3/8"	54.5	12.615	0.1546

Spot Fluid on bottom with fluid already in hole.

Factor x height of fluid=amount to spot

4 1/2" x 2 3/8"=.00525
4 1/2" x 2 7/8"=.00987
5 1/2" x 2 3/8"=.00466
5 1/2" x 2 7/8"=.00783
7" x 2 3/8"=.00428
7" x 2 7/8"=.00679

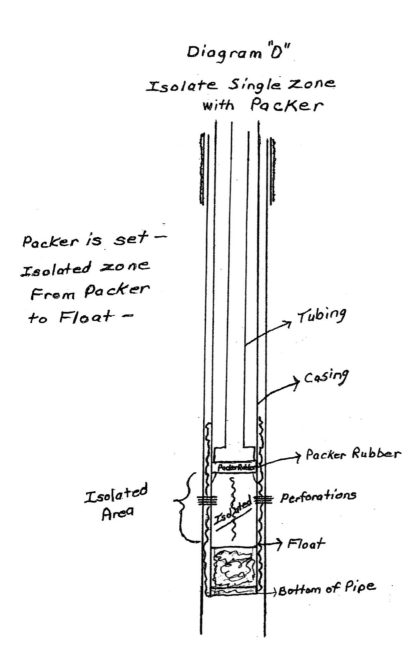

Diagram "D"

Isolate Single Zone
with Packer

Packer is set —
Isolated zone
From Packer
to Float —

Tubing

Casing

Packer Rubber

Isolated
Area

Perforations

Float

Bottom of Pipe

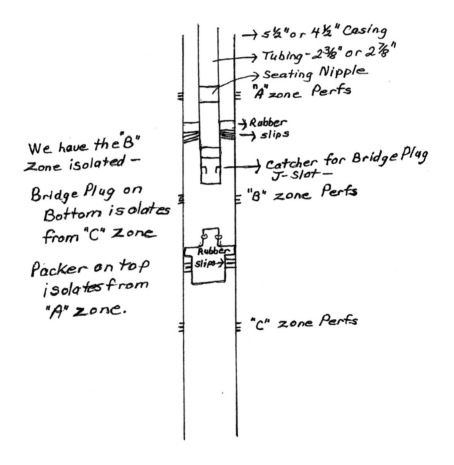

Diagram "E"
Isolation of "B" Zone
with Bridge Plug and Packer

→ 5½" or 4½" Casing
→ Tubing - 2⅜" or 2⅞"
→ Seating Nipple
"A" zone Perfs

→ Rubber
→ slips

We have the "B"
Zone isolated –

→ Catcher for Bridge Plug
J-Slot –

"B" zone Perfs

Bridge Plug on
Bottom isolates
from "C" Zone

Rubber
Slips →

Packer on top
isolates from
"A" zone.

"C" zone Perfs

7

SUBSURFACE LOOK,
TANK BATTERY, AND LINES

First let's look at the subsurface equipment. Once casing has been set, usually 4 1/2" or 5 1/2" casing, the well has been completed, it looks something like the diagram in exhibit A.

The casing has been set through the productive zones, usually a few feet off bottom. The bottom of the drilled hole is called the rotary total depth (RTD). When the well was completed, the bottom was not drilled out. It should be close to the float. This is called the plug back total depth (PBTD.).

The tubing has been run in the well. The first thing run in the hole is a mud anchor. This is a cut off joint of tubing orange peeled on the end. This can be any length, but I usually run about a 15' mud anchor. This mud anchor has either holes, or slots in the top 3'. This is where the fluid comes into the tubing and pump. The mud anchor helps to keep trash out of the pump, by letting trash drop into the bottom of the mud anchor.

Right above the mud anchor is a 1.1' seating nipple, which the bottom of an insert pump would seat into. This is also where a mandrel on a tubing swab will stop and not go through. If you have a tubing pump, your barrel would go here instead of a seating nipple. From here you run your tubing that comes in 30' to 33' joints. At the top of the tubing you have a flow T, with a 2" or 3" threaded end on one side and a 1" threaded end on the other side. The 2" or 3" hooks to the lead line. The 1" is called the bleeder.

Now you run the insert pump, or plunger if it is a tubing pump, on either 3/4" or 7/8" rods. There are also other sizes of rods, from 1/2" to 1", but you won't see too many of these. The bottom of the pump has seating cups that seat into the seating nipple. If it is a tubing pump, the plunger goes into the barrel. On the insert pump, usually a 2' pony rod is put on top of the pump. This acts as a stabilizer, compared to a 25' rod. Rods are then run to surface. Rods come in 25' lengths. When you get to the top, the pump must be spaced out correctly for it to work as it should. To do this, you use pony rods that come in 2' to 10' lengths. On the very top of the rod string, you use a polish rod, which is either 1 1/8" to 1 1/4". This is spaced so the polish rod will never come out of the stuffing box. A liner is run on the polish rod. This is the shinny part you see going up and down when you pull up to a pumping well. The length of this liner is determined by the length of the stroke of the pumping unit. It needs to be long enough so that it will not come out of the stuffing box, also. Rubbers are inserted into the stuffing box and tightened down with bolts. These rubbers are installed so nothing leaks out the top. They tighten around the liner. When the well is pumping correctly, and the fluid is at surface, the oil actually helps lubricate the well head so it won't leak. This is the part of the well that you see going up and down at the well head. The polish rod extends out of the liner and is hooked to the pumping unit with Clamps above the Reins coming off the horse head of the pumping unit.

One thing to note here. There are several kinds of pumps. The insert pump is the smallest of pumps, and pumps the least amount of fluid. In Kansas, we run a lot of these. It can handle anywhere from 1 barrel per day to 400 to 500 barrel per day, depending on the stroke length. Next we have the tubing pump. It can handle larger amounts of fluid. We can still go to an oversized tubing pump with an on-off tool. Then we go to REDA pumps, which have motors on the bottom of the tubing downhole, and screw pumps, which can handle 5,000 to 10,000 barrels of fluid per day. These will be explained in more detail in the pump section.

That should give you a good idea what is under ground and at the well head. Fluid is pumped up the tubing to the lead line through the pump at the bottom of the hole. Now we'll explain the surface equipment. Also, take a look at exhibit B, which gives you some idea of the well at the surface.

Most people have the impression that above ground vessels, such as gun barrels and separators are very advanced systems and quite complicated. This could not be further from the truth. Most of these vessels are quite simple and use basic principles of nature. They are what I call "common sense" vessels. Let me explain how these all function.

As mentioned earlier, fluid is pumped up the tubing to the well head, through the pump in the bottom of the hole. Once it gets to the well head, it goes into the lead line over to the gun barrel, the largest of the vessels at the tank battery. You will see this in exhibit C.

How does this vessel work? Take a look at exhibit D. The fluid, gas, oil and water, is pumped down the lead line over to the gun barrel. The fluid goes into the gun barrel with a riser that goes to the top of the gun barrel into the flume. From here the fluid goes down to the bottom of the vessel, where it goes out through a spreader inside the bottom of the vessel. The oil, water and gas separates. Gas bubbles go up and out the vent on the top of the vessel. Remember, oil floats on water, so it rises to the top of the vessel. Most gun barrels carry a 3' to 4' oil pad on top of the water. The produced oil runs out the top of the vessel and over to the stock tanks that store the oil for transportation to the purchaser.

To this point, everything works fairly simply, but what about the water? A siphon is used. This siphon works with air pressure. It is closed at the top. You can regulate the amount of oil carried in the gun barrel by dropping a slotted 4' to 5' piece of PVC piping down in the top of the siphon. Thus, if you want to carry more or less oil on top of the water in the gun barrel, you just change out the piece with a slot either higher or lower. Over the years, these risers and siphons have been vastly improved. At one time, most risers and siphons were on the outside of the vessel. On low fluid wells, in the winter, they would have a tendency to freeze up. All the new gun barrels have both of them on the inside. Remember, the fluid coming out of the well is warm. This helps keep the lines from freezing. The only problem is when you develop a problem with one of these lines, now the gun barrel must be emptied and cleaned before you can repair them.

These are very balanced vessels. Nature pretty well takes care of everything. The oil levels will fluctuate some, but not much. You can gauge the oil level in the gun barrel by what we call canning the gun barrel. You climb to the top of the gun barrel and tie your gauge line, to say, a bean or coffee can. Lower the coffee can or bean can into the oil and let it fill up. Now slowly lower the can until it begins to float. This will be the oil/water contact point in the vessel. Pull the gauge line and measure the distance to the first oil point, to the bottom of the can. This will give you the amount of oil you are carrying on top of the gun barrel.

It is very important that all of this be working correctly. The gun barrel will need to be cleaned periodically, either the oil will build up a cake, or solids will fall to bottom and disrupt the spreader so that you begin getting bad oil. Once in a while you can get by with cleaning over the top, if it is strictly a cake problem. Otherwise, the vessel will have to be emptied, clean out plate removed, and the vessel jet cleaned.

As oil and water separate, the water runs to the water tank and the oil goes into the stock tanks. Remember, the oil level in the gun barrel stays almost constant. Thus, if the well makes 20 bbl per day total fluid, 5 oil and 15 water, that should be what you will make in each vessel per day. The normal gun barrel is either metal, fiberglass, or wood. The most common size is 210 bbl. The gun barrel will be the tallest tank at the tank battery.

If a lease has its own disposal well, there won't always be a water tank at the tank battery. The water tank may be at the disposal well itself, or it can be piped right into the well from the water line off the gun barrel. I would not recommend running it directly into the disposal well from the gun barrel, but some people do. It's a lot better to have a settling tank because of the solids and also because a minuscule percentage of oil can easily be carried in the water line. This will definitely slow down your disposal well.

Normally, there will be a vent on top of the flume and one on top of the gun barrel, so that any gas from the well is released to the atmosphere. Usually the stock tanks will have vents on them also. Often times they may be tied to the gun barrel venting system.

Gun barrels come in various sizes. Wooden gun barrels are very old, and not made anymore. They have become obsolete. Remember, these vessels must allow time for the oil, gas, and water to separate. There are two factors to separation. Volume is the first. If you are moving an extreme amount of fluid (water), this will not allow enough time for the oil to break out of the water in a small vessel. A rule of thumb is 2.5 times the per day volume of the vessel, would be the maximum amount to have enough time for the oil to break out. Thus, in a 210 bbl gun barrel, you would not like to run much more than 500 bbl per day through it. The second factor is gravity of the oil. If the gravity is low, say 20 gravity, then it will take longer to separate out from the water. This will also play into the size of the vessel needed.

When establishing a new lease, it is very important that the tank battery be set on the highest elevation possible. This is for one simple reason, it's a heck of a lot cheaper to run a water line to a disposal well than to have it hauled. In other words, almost all wells will make some water sooner or later. You need a place to get rid of it. This is salt water, not freshwater, so it has to be disposed of into another well, which we call a salt water disposal well. It only makes sense to use gravity to get the salt water from the tank battery to the disposal well.

Another important factor when deciding where to set your tank battery, is accessibility for trucking. This may not be necessary in every area of the world, but in Kansas, most of the pipelines have been shut down. You definitely need a way to get it sold. Often, trucking is the only way out.

Instead of a gun barrel, sometimes a separator will be used. Attached, you will find an exhibit E, of a separator. This vessel is operated by pressure and a float system. This vessel can be used to move water over a hill because it does use pressure. This is one advantage.

These are usually much smaller vessels, but they can handle a lot of fluid. Often, if you have a lease making 1,000 to 5,000 bbl of fluid per day, you will have a separator first and then a gun barrel as a settling tank before you go to a stock tank. This makes it possible to produce large amounts of water.

Tanks batteries can take care of more than one well. They take care of a whole lease. In other words, there could be several wells going into the same gun barrel and tank battery. There will only be one tank battery per oil lease. As long as the landowners royalty interest is exactly the same, then this can all be one tank battery. All the wells on this particular lease will go into the same tank battery.

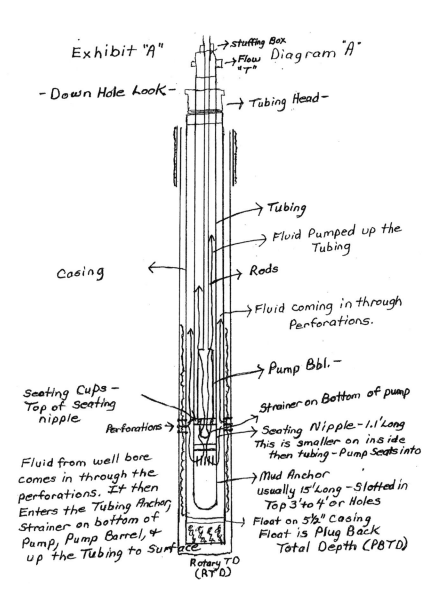

Exhibit "A"

Diagram "A"

- Down Hole Look -

→ Stuffing Box

→ Flow "T"

→ Tubing Head -

→ Tubing

→ Fluid Pumped up the Tubing

Casing

→ Rods

→ Fluid coming in through Perforations.

→ Pump Bbl. -

Seating Cups –
Top of Seating
nipple

Strainer on Bottom of pump

Perforations →

→ Seating Nipple – 1.1' Long
This is smaller on inside
then tubing - Pump Seats into

Fluid from well bore
comes in through the
perforations. It then
Enters the Tubing Anchor,
Strainer on bottom of
Pump, Pump Barrel, &
up the Tubing to Surface

→ Mud Anchor
usually 15' Long – Slotted in
Top 3' to 4' or Holes

→ Float on 5½" Casing
Float is Plug Back
Total Depth (PBTD)

Rotary TD
(RTD)

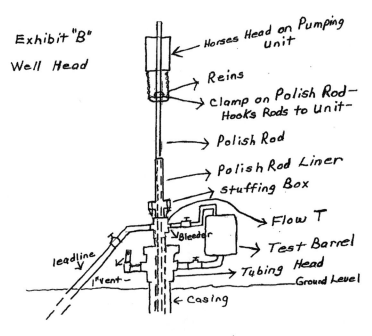

Exhibit "B"

Well Head

- Horses Head on Pumping Unit
- Reins
- Clamp on Polish Rod — Hooks Rods to Unit —
- Polish Rod
- Polish Rod Liner
- Stuffing Box
- Flow T
- Bleeder
- Test Barrel
- leadline
- Tubing Head
- Ground Level
- 1" vent —
- Casing

— Pumping Unit —

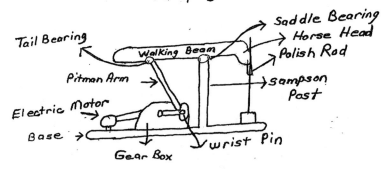

- Tail Bearing
- Saddle Bearing
- Horse Head
- Polish Rod
- Walking Beam
- Pitman Arm
- Sampson Post
- Electric Motor
- Base →
- wrist Pin
- Gear Box

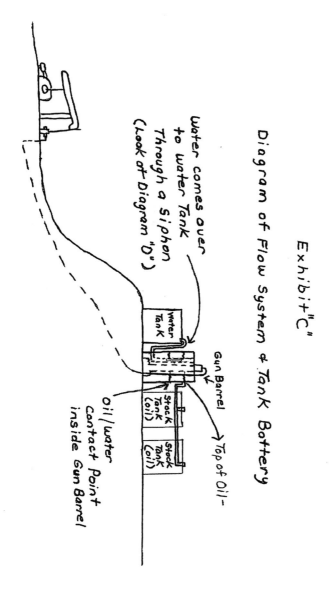

Exhibit "C"

Diagram of Flow System & Tank Battery

Water comes over
to water Tank
Through a Siphon
(Look at Diagram "D")

Gun Barrel

Top of Oil-

Water Tank

Stock Tank (oil)

Stock Tank (oil)

Oil/water
contact Point
inside Gun Barrel

Exhibit "D"

– Gun Barrel –

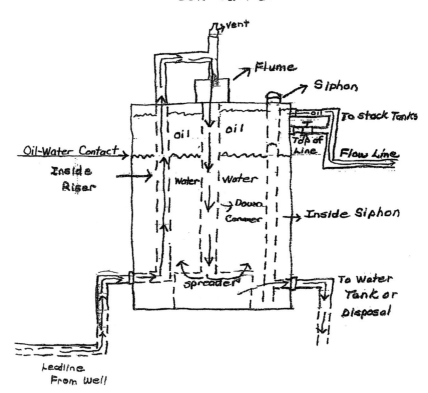

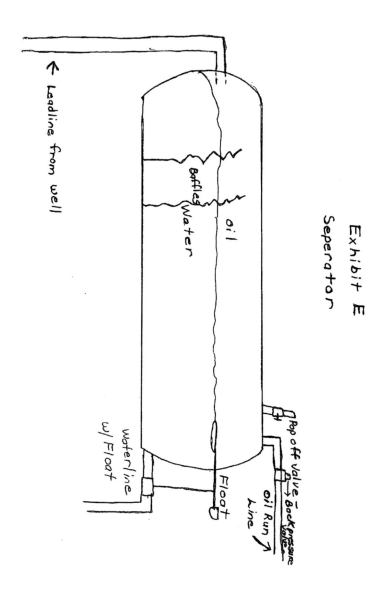

8

THE PUMPER

The pumper is an important part of the maintenance of the well on a daily basis. He goes by the lease, and each well, every day of the year.

The first thing he does is go by the tank battery and gauge the production from the day before. He runs a gauge line and just lightly tags the bottom of the stock tank. He then pulls the gauge line to see where the oil is on the line. This amount is the gauge for the day. To figure out what you had for production, you subtract yesterdays gauge and this will tell you. There are usually two stock tanks on each lease, and maybe more if you are making lots of oil. You can tell which tank you are running into by looking at the configuration of the flow line valves, or simply by listening to see which tank the oil is running into. Each tank has a valve coming off the gun barrel flow line. One will be open and the other shut, in less it is the end tank, farthest from the gun barrel, in which case they may both be open since the oil will flow into the first tank. The tanks are also tied together by overflow lines that should be opened. Once a tank gets full, it will automatically flow into the next tank through the overflow lines. This way you don't have to be on site when one tank becomes full. You can close the flow line on the full tank and open the empty tank the next day. Once you have a full tank, a gauger, usually the truck driver, will come by and make sure the oil is good, and load the oil out of the tank into his truck. The tank of oil has then been sold.

Normally, we have two sizes of stock tanks, a 10' (high) × 12' (diameter)- 200 barrel tanks, which measures approximately 1.67 bbl per inch or 20 bbl per foot, or a 15' (high) × 10' (diameter)- 210 barrel tank, which measures 1.16 bbl per inch or 14 bbl per foot. There are other sizes, but we don't find two many of those left in operations nowadays. No matter what the size, the oil purchaser will strap the tank so that they know exactly how much oil is going to be purchased. They will give you a tank table once this is done. This is how the pumper knows exactly how much is made each day, along with the amount that is sold when they pick it up. The gauger will leave a run ticket on location when he picks up a tank of oil. It will have the ticket number, the starting gauge and an ending gauge, along with the percentage of bullshit (BS), or water. From this the pumper will figure out how much they have taken and this will be recorded on his gauge sheet.

Attached, you will find a copy of a gauge report, exhibit A. A good pumper will try to go by each lease about the same time each day so that the gauges level out for a day. This gauge will be the first thing that will tell the pumper whether he has any problems with the well. The well should make about the same production every day. If it doesn't, then you usually have problems.

At the tank battery, he should look around and make sure he has no leaks. He might want to check the water tank and make sure there is plenty of room for the next day. Also, he might want to make sure fluid is coming to the gun barrel from the well.

Now you go to the well. Check the well head for leaks. The rubbers in the stuffing box will wear out, or down, so he may have to tighten the bolts on the stuffing box to stop a leak. When the rubbers wear out, they need to be pulled and changed out. A good pumper will usually have these with him.

Next he opens up the bleeder, the 1" valve coming off the flow T. The well should pump fluid out this line if the well is pumping correctly. There are two other options. There may be no fluid at all.

More than likely, you have a downhole problem. The second option is the bleeder is on a vacuum. In this case, more than likely, you have a tubing leak downhole. Other possibilities, if you have no fluid, the rods may be parted. In other words, the rods have been pulled apart. Often, when this happens, you may get a little blow and suck, but no fluid. You could also have pump problems. They do have a tendency to wear out. The pump may be stuck and is unseating from the seating nipple. These are just a few things that can go wrong. You can also tell a lot by how the pumping unit is acting. If it is rod heavy or pulling way too hard, it is either parted or a stuck pump, or a pump that is about to get stuck. It makes things a lot easier when you go out to pull the well, if you have some idea what is wrong. A good pumper can usually tell you. At this point, the pumper will call the production man and let him know what he thinks is wrong. The production man will usually take it from here.

Lots of companies have barrels hooked to the annulus (The 2" valve coming off the 5 1/2" or 4 1/2" tubing head). The annulus is the area between the 5 1/2" casing on the inside, and the 2 7/8" or 2 3/8" tubing on the outside. The 1" bleeder from the flow T is going open ended into the top of the barrel. In my opinion, this is the way most pumping wells should be hooked up.

This way when you open the bleeder to see if the well is pumping, the fluid goes into the barrel instead of on the ground. The barrel can then be emptied down the backside (annulus) of the well and will be pumped back up the hole. There is a valve coming off the bottom of the barrel to the 2" connection on the casing head that can be closed and opened.

Now let's say you didn't have the production at the tank battery that you thought you should have. With the barrel at the well, it is easy to barrel test the well. To do this, you time how long it takes to fill the barrel to a point. Remember, most of these barrels that are put on the well hold 55 gallons. One barrel of oil is 42 gallons. You can get a good idea what 42 gallons would be and that will be the mark you will fill the drum to. Many pumpers have a rod that they can put into the 55-gallon barrel with a mark indicting 42 gallons. You would start with the valve open on the bottom of the drum so that when you open the 1" bleeder, the fluid will run right through the drum. You do this because you will usually have a surge when you open the bleeder because the lead line has some pressure on it to run it over to the gun barrel. Once the surge is off, you close the barrel on the bottom and time how long it take to catch a barrel full (42 gallons). Now you divide the number of minutes into 1,440 minutes (minutes in a day), and this gives you the number of barrels per day the well is producing. This will give you a fairly accurate idea. To do it perfectly, you would need to hold the same amount of lead line pressure on the bleeder as you are while running the test. For all practical purposes, this should be good enough. If it does not have a barrel, you can use a 5-gallon bucket and time it and figure out how long it would take you to fill a 42 gallon barrel, and do the same thing. This can get a little messy. Usually, unless this is a high fluid well, the pump will produce somewhere between 80% to 90% of the barrel test you have just taken.

There are several things that could cause the fluid to be off somewhat. First of all, the pump could be worn. When this happens, we say it needs a pump change. You could have a small hole or a split in the tubing. Once the well goes off, it's no longer the pumpers problem. He calls his boss and they take care of it from there.

The pumper also maintains the pumping unit in some cases, but not as much as they use to. They use to grease the unit, change oil in the gearboxes, change sheaves to slow down or speed up the unit, change belts, and so on. Nowadays, almost all pumpers in our area are what we call contract pumpers, where they own their own pickups and pay for their own repairs and gas to do the job, along with insurance and taxes. They get paid so much a month to go by these wells every day. In order to make a decent living, they need to have a lot of wells. They can't afford to spend a lot of time at one well. Years ago most of the pumpers were company pumpers who worked only for one company and their vehicle was paid for, but that has changed. Usually, when something goes wrong, or any type of maintenance that takes any time at all, a roustabout crew is called out to do the work. Contract pumpers are paid so much per stop per month. In other words, let's say that a contract pumper is paid $100 per stop per month. Say you have a one well lease. The pumper would be paid $100 to go by the well and

$100 for the tank battery per month. Thus, he would be paid $200 per month for this lease. He gets $100 for every time he stops per day.

Let's say you go to the tank battery and you have no fluid coming into the stock tank. You check the gun barrel and you have no fluid coming into it either. Then you go to the well and you have fluid at the bleeder. You see no leaks at either place. It is time to start looking for a lead line leak. You follow the lead line from the well to the gun barrel and you find a leak. You run back and shut the well down and call your boss. It's time for a backhoe and roustabout company to come out and repair the leak and clean up the mess.

The job of the pumper is a trouble shooter. He goes to work every day hoping everything is running correctly. He knows in the back of his mind, that someday things won't be going smooth, and he is going to have trouble.

A few years ago, it was the pumper responsibility to treat the wells with chemical. Chemical is used for corrosion. The pumper would dump 5 gallons or so of corrosion inhibitor down the backside and circulate the well through what we call the circulating valves. This circulating system consists of the 1" bleeder being hooked into the 2" on the tubing head so that the chemical will drop down into the annulus. You would open both valves and close the valve to the test barrel. From here, you let the well pump for a few hours so the chemical comes clear around and coats the outside and inside of the tubing and rods. This helps stop the corrosion on the metal. Today, most of the treating is done by a chemical truck. They come around a least once a month and dump chemical and a little lease water down the backside. The well is no longer circulated. This works fairly well on low fluid wells, but can be a real problem in high fluid wells. One reason for this, as I mentioned before, is the fact that a pumper needs to have 30 to 60 wells per day to make a living. He does not have time to put a well on circulation and come back two hours later and put the well back on production.

Almost all wells make some amount of salt water. In certain areas, this water can be very corrosive. Also, when you mix waters from different formations, they are usually not real compatible. In our area, it is very common, to have multiple zones opened. This is called commingling of zones.

Another problem is that the oil maybe heavy and tough to get separated out from the water. There are chemicals that can be used to enhance this. Usually this is done at the well head by continuous treatment by using a chemical pump. It is hooked to the backside of the well and a small amount of chemical is pumped down the annulus or into the lead line on each stroke of the pumping unit. The chemical pump operates off the walking beam by the up and down motion of the unit. This pump can be regulated at so many gallons per day. The pumper must make sure it is working daily. He needs to keep a close eye on how much it uses and when it needs to be filled.

A good pumper can tell when you are getting all the fluid the well can produce. We call this pumped off or pounding. Sometimes you can see this when you drive up to the well. As the well is on the down-stroke, you can see the reins wiggle. This is called the pound. What is happening is that when the bottom ball and seat on the pump opens on the up stroke, the barrel is not completely filling when the top ball opens on the downstroke and heads down. The plunger then hits the fluid in the barrel. In other words, the barrel does not fill completely, so there is a void before you hit fluid. This is the pound. Sometimes you can't see it, so as the well polish rod goes down, you grab hold of the polish rod and feel it. Thus you can actually feel the pound.

This pretty well sums up the duties of the pumper, except for the book work. Attached, you will see how the pumper report books are kept and balanced, by exhibit B. Each company has a little different system, but they all serve the same purpose.

The job of the pumper has vastly changed over the last 40 years. My father was a company pumper. He did a lot more physical labor than a contract pumper does nowadays. In addition, many companies have their tank batteries hooked up with remote gauging devices in which they can view these measurements on the Internet and receive live time measurements. I'm not sure I like this idea because the pumper can usually access this and he may feel that he does not have to go by the tank battery that day. We are getting so automated that one day the pumper may be eliminated. Hopefully, this will not happen. I personally believe we still need to go by these leases daily. We don't need big messes.

Exhibit "A"

MONTHLY LEASE REPORT

| LEASE | | | | | MONTH | |
| PUMPER | | | | | YEAR | |

TANK GAUGES / PRODUCTION / PIPELINE RUNS

| | TANK # & SIZE | | | TANK # & SIZE | | | TANK # & SIZE | | | TOTAL STOCK BARRELS | PRODUCTION | | | DATE | TANK NUMBER | TICKET NUMBER | OPENING STOCK | | CLOSING STOCK | | GROSS BARRELS |
	FT	IN	BBLS	FT	IN	BBLS	FT	IN	BBLS		FT	IN	BBLS				FT	IN	FT	IN	
1																					
2																					
3																					
4																					
5																					
6																					
7														B.S. & TANK BOTTOMS REMOVED							
8																					
9																					
10																					
11																					
12														WELL TEST DATA							
13																					
14																					
15																					
16																					
17																					
18																					
19																					
20																					
21																					
22																					
23																					
24														GUN BARREL REPORT							
25														FREE OIL / CAKE / TOTAL FLUID / REMARKS							
26														REMARKS			PIPELINE RUNS +				
27																	ENDING STOCK				
28																	OTHER DISPOSALS				
29																	TOTAL =				
30																	BEG. STOCK -				
31														MONTHLY WATER PRODUCED (BBLS)			PRODUCTION =				

Exhibit "B"

MONTHLY LEASE REPORT

| LEASE | Mudd Lease | | MONTH | Feb. |
| PUMPER | Terry Piesker | | YEAR | 1986 |

TANK GAUGES / PRODUCTION / PIPELINE RUNS

| | TANK # & SIZE 5594 200 | | | TANK # & SIZE 5595 200 | | | TANK # & SIZE | | | TOTAL STOCK BARRELS 150 | PROD. | | | DATE | TANK NUMBER | TICKET NUMBER | OPENING STOCK | | CLOSING STOCK | | GROSS BARRELS |
	FT	IN	BBLS	FT	IN	BBLS	FT	IN	BBLS		FT	IN	BBLS				FT	IN	FT	IN	
1	8	3		1	1						1	10	36.67	2-3	5594	299100/09	9	5	1	2	165
2	9	5		1	9						1	10	36.67	2-9	5595	131	9	4	1	4	160
3	1	2		3	7						1	10	36.67	2-15	5594	136	9	4	1	1	165
4	1	2		5	5						1	10	36.67	2-19	5595	154	9	4	1	1	165
5	1	2		9	1						3	8	93.33	2-22	5594	168	9	4	1	2	168.33
6	1	4		9	5						6	10		2-26	5595	184	9	5	1	3	163.33
7	3	0		9	5						1	8	33.33								
8	4	5		9	5						1	5	28.33		B.S. & TANK BOTTOMS REMOVED						
9	6	2		1	4						1	9	35								
10	7	8		1	4						1	6	30								
11	9	5		1	7						2	0	40								
12	9	5		3	1						1	6	30		WELL TEST DATA						
13	9	5		4	8						1	7	31.67								
14	9	5		6	10						2	2	43.33								
15	1	1		7	7						9		15								
16	2	7		9	5						3	4	66.67								
17	3	8		9	5						1	1	21.67								
18	5	4		9	5						1	8	33.33								
19	7			1	1						1	8	33.33								
20	8	6		1	1						1	6	30								
21	9	5		8	1						1	11	38.33								
22	9	5		3	7						1	6	30								
23	1	2		5	3						1	8	33.33								
24	1	2		7	9						2	6	50		GUN BARREL REPORT						
25	2	1		9	5						2	7	51.67		FREE OIL / CAKE / TOTAL FLUID / REMARKS						
26	4	0		1	2						1	11	38.33		REMARKS		PIPELINE RUNS +			981.66	
27	5	8		1	3						1	8	33.33				ENDING STOCK			171.67	
28	7	4		1	3					171.67	1	8	33.33				OTHER DISPOSALS				
29																	TOTAL =			1153.33	
30																	BEG. STOCK -			150	
31														MONTHLY WATER PRODUCED (BBLS)			PRODUCTION =			1003.33	

118

9

DOWNHOLE PUMPS

The are several kinds of downhole pumps that can be used to get gas, oil, and water to the surface. You need to have some idea what your well will produce before you can make the right choice on what kind of pump you need to run into your well. In Kansas, probably 80% of the pumps in the hole are rod pumps, with pumping units at the surface. You can move a little fluid, or you can move a lot of fluid with these types of pumps. We will start out with the simplest of all, the insert pump.

The bottom hold-down insert pump is the most popular of all basic pumps. Attached is diagram A, a bottom hold-down pump. The hold-down is located on the bottom of the pump. The pump is run in the hole on the inside of the tubing on sucker rods. Once the pump is on bottom, it seats into what we call a seating nipple. The seating nipple is a little bit smaller than the inside of the tubing. The seating cups on the outside of the pump, located on the bottom of the pump, seat into the seating nipple. Once the pump has been seated into the seating nipple, the rig will long stroke the well. By long stroke, I mean make the pump go up and down, giving you a blow out the bleeder. You are now lifting fluid.

Let me explain how the pump actually works. Here again, we are working with very basic principles. Pumps operate with balls and seats. Take a look at diagram A. Right above the seating cups, on the inside of the pump, there is a ball and seat. Below this ball and seat, is a strainer with an opening that allows the fluid from below the seating nipple to enter the inside of the pump. Fluid comes through this ball and seat as the plunger moves up the hole. Notice that the plunger also has a ball and seat and as the plunger goes up, the ball and seat closes off and you pull the fluid up through the pump and into the inside of the tubing. Now when the plunger is going down the bottom ball and seat closes and the ball and seat on the plunger opens up. These balls and seats work in unison, one open and the other closed, depending on what direction the plunger is moving. This is how the oil, gas, and water is pumped to the surface. Diagram B depicts this. The plunger length is determined by depth. Usually the plunger will be about 1' long for every 1,000' of depth. In other words, if the well is 3,000' deep, the plunger would be 3' long. If the well is 4,000' deep, the plunger would be 4' long, and so on. The plunger moves up and down in the barrel. Most of the pumps that we work with are call metal to metal insert pumps because the barrel and the plungers are metal. They are what we call Precision pumps. They are very close tolerance pumps. This means the plunger and barrel are very tight fitting. The fluid moves through the bottom ball and seat, up through the barrel, inside the plunger and out through the top of the barrel. The pumping unit at the surface operates this plunger, making it go up and down. The length of the barrel is determined by the stroke length of the pumping unit. The longer the stroke, the longer the barrel length. Once this pump is seated in the seating nipple, it will never move. The barrel will be stationary. In order to space this pump out correctly, the pulling unit crew will come down and find the bottom of the pump. He will then mark it. He will come up and find the top and mark it. Now he will space the plunger out so that it will not tag bottom or hit on top. They usually leave them 12" off bottom because the rods will stretch a little when the fluid gets pumped down. He uses pony rods (short rods of 2' to 10') to space this out correctly using the polish rod on top that will be tied to the pumping unit.

The bottom hold-down insert pump is the most popular of the basic pumps. This is due to its ruggedness and relative simplicity. As noted, the hold-down is located on the bottom of the pump. The discharge of the pump is at a stationary point at the top of the pump, located the length of the pump away from the bottom hold-down. The stagnant area for this type of pump can lead to corrosion of the outside of the pump barrel or allow sand or other particles to build up and stick the pump in the tubing. Diagram C is a bottom hold-down pump.

The second type of pump is the top hold-down insert pump. This is a popular pump in areas that produce sand or other particles that tend to accumulate over the bottom hold-down. The fluid discharge point of this type of pump is only inches away from the location of the hold-down. There is not a stagnant fluid area between the hold-down and the fluid discharge point. The top hold-down pump is not as rugged as the bottom hold-down pump since the outside of the pump is only subjected to formation pressure. Diagram D is a top hold-down pump.

The third type of pump is the traveling barrel insert pump. This pump is useful in pumping conditions that are characterized by relatively heavy particles. The traveling barrel helps to keep sand or other particles in movement above the hold-down, located on the bottom of the pump, reducing the possibility of a stuck pump. The traveling valve is located on the top of the pump so that it automatically closes in times of pump inactivity, preventing anything from settling inside the pump. The trade off for this advantage is that the pump is not as good for gas compression as the two stationary barrel insert pumps, and that the pumping pressure is balanced on a pull tube that can bow and cause extra pump friction and wear on the pull tube. Diagram E depicts a traveling barrel insert pump.

The fourth type of pump is the tubing pump. This pump can handle much more fluid. It is the most rugged of the four pumps due to its heavy wall construction. This is what you run in a well that makes a lot of total fluid. The barrel is run on the bottom of the tubing. It has a separate standing valve, which is dropped in the hole once the tubing is on bottom. You then run a plunger on the rods. This type of pump will have extensions on the top and bottom and when spaced correctly, the plunger can stroke out into these extensions allowing the plunger to be washed clean during the up and down stroke. When this type of pump is pulled, you can run down to the seating nipple and screw into it and pull the plunger and standing valve. However, in order to change the barrel, the tubing must be pulled out of the hole. I know people who refuse to run this type of pump just because of this. Standard pump sizes for 2 3/8" (2") tubing are 1 3/4" plungers and for 2 7/8" (2 1/2") tubing and 2 1/4" plungers. Also, you can run oversized equipment like 2 3/4" tubing pumps, which will have on and off tools on the top of them. To do any work at all on these types of pumps, you would have to pull the tubing. These pumps can move a lot of fluid. Depending on the size and stroke length, these types of pumps can move 150 to 1,000 barrels of fluid per day. Diagram F depicts the tubing pump.

One of the unique features of the tubing pump is the fact that you can run an insert pump back in the hole and it will seat right in the top of the tubing pump barrel. Say you had a well that was producing 200 BFPD and it slowly went down to say 100 BFPD. Your tubing pump wears out and you decide to pull it. You go down and try to grab hold of the standing valve and you cannot get it. This happens quite often as a matter of fact. Crap will get on this standing valve and you cannot get it to come loose. Since your fluid has dropped off, now you can get by with an insert pump. You do not need to pull the standing valve. This standing valve will work fine with the insert pump that you are going to run back in the hole. The standing valve will simply work as a back up to the bottom valve on the insert pump. Thus, you go ahead and pull the plunger and simply run an insert pump and respace the well and put it back on the pump. Now if you were going to go ahead and pull the barrel out of the hole and you could not get the standing valve, this would mean that you would have to pull wet tubing. Wet tubing means that as you break every joint out of the hole, it will be full of water and or oil. You ask why is this? This is because the standing valve is the valve that holds the fluid in place in the tubing. One way to get away from this is to swab the tubing down and put it right down the backside to the well. The pulling unit hands will love you for this.

Pulling a wet string is no fun for them, especially in the winter. They are going to get wet no matter what, if the string is wet.

Those are the main types of pumps you will see in Kansas. We do have a lot of wells that do produce a lot of water. Some of these wells would produce as much as 5,000 bbl per day. That is a lot of fluid. The types of pumps mentioned above cannot handle this amount of fluid. For wells such as these we have Reda pumps and screw-type pumps. These are very expensive. They run anywhere from $25,000 to as much as $80,000. You had better be producing a pretty good percentage of oil to be able to afford the expense of this type of pump.

I am not going to go into a lot of detail on these, but the Reda pump consists of a downhole pump that is put on the end of the tubing. It is a submersible pump that is powered by a submersed motor and electricity. Thus, a cable is run alongside the tubing down to the bottom of the hole. This electric line is connected to the pump at the bottom of the hole. This type of pump needs fluid over it at all times or you will burn up the motor. These types of pumps, depending on the size of the pump and tubing, can move large amounts of fluid. Besides the cost of the unit itself, your electric costs will be enormous. You had better know what you have before you ever put one of these in the hole. There are several of these running, but I am not sure how economical they are with regards to the amount of oil they make. Obviously they must make money or the operator would not put up with the hassle.

Secondly, we have screw pumps. These are a lot like Redas in the respect that they can move a lot of fluid. On these types of pumps, instead of a metal barrel on bottom, you have what we call a stator. This stator is a rather large piece of pipe that is lined with a very hard rubber. It is run on the bottom of your tubing. You then run what we call a rotor, which looks like a corkscrewed piece of chrome on the end of your rods. This goes into the stator and rotates in the stator and lifts the fluid to surface by rotating the fluid up the hole. On the surface you have a device that fits on the top of the rods and rotates the rods and the rotor inside the stator, thus pumping the fluid to surface. These run around $30,000, depending on how much fluid you need to make. These are powered by an electric motor on the surface. It usually takes a pretty good size motor to run these pumps. Your electric costs will be pretty high.

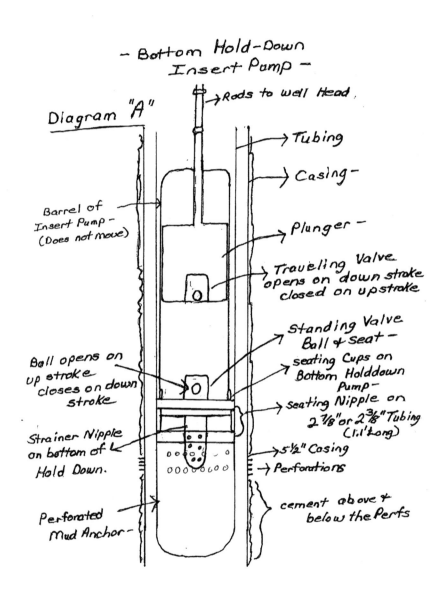

- Bottom Hold-Down Insert Pump -

Diagram "A"

→ Rods to well Head.

→ Tubing

→ Casing -

Barrel of
Insert Pump -
(Does not move)

→ Plunger -

Traveling Valve
opens on down stroke
closed on upstroke

Standing Valve
Ball & Seat -
seating Cups on
Bottom Holddown
Pump -
seating Nipple on
2 7/8" or 2 3/8" Tubing
(1.1' Long)

Ball opens on
up stroke
closes on down
stroke

5 1/2" Casing
Perforations

Strainer Nipple
on bottom of
Hold Down.

Perforated
Mud Anchor -

cement above &
below the Perfs

Diagram "B"

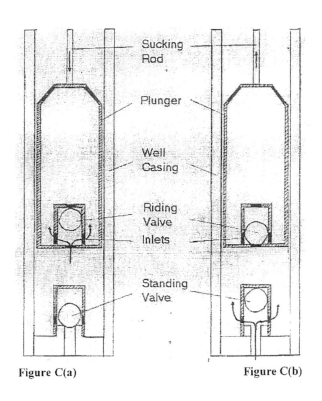

Sucking Rod

Plunger

Well Casing

Riding Valve

Inlets

Standing Valve

Figure C(a)   Figure C(b)

Diagram "F"
— Tubing Pump —

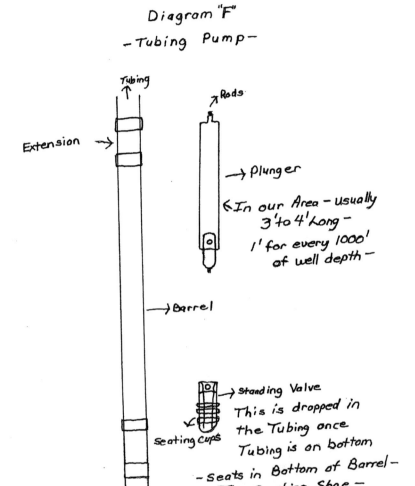

Tubing

Extension →

Rods

→ Plunger

← In our Area — usually
3' to 4' Long —
1' for every 1000'
of well depth —

→ Barrel

→ Standing Valve
This is dropped in
the Tubing once
Tubing is on bottom
— Seats in Bottom of Barrel —
The Seating Shoe —

Seating cups

THE INNER WORKINGS OF THE OIL AND GAS BUSINESS

Bottom Hold-Down Insert Pumps, Thin Wall (RWB) and Heavy Wall (RHB)   Page 1 of 1

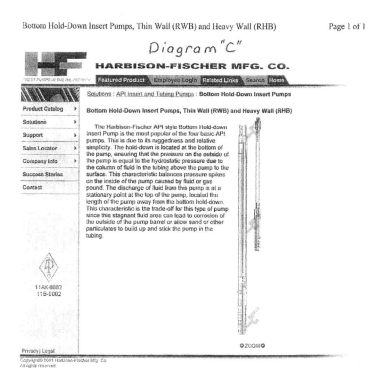

Diagram "C"

HARBISON-FISCHER MFG. CO.

BEST PUMPS IN THE OIL PATCH

Featured Product | Employee Login | Related Links | Search | Home

Solutions : API Insert and Tubing Pumps : **Bottom Hold-Down Insert Pumps**

Product Catalog ▶
Solutions ▶
Support ▶
Sales Locator ▶
Company Info ▶
Success Stories
Contact

Bottom Hold-Down Insert Pumps, Thin Wall (RWB) and Heavy Wall (RHB)

The Harbison-Fischer API style Bottom Hold-down Insert Pump is the most popular of the four basic API pumps. This is due to its ruggedness and relative simplicity. The hold-down is located at the bottom of the pump, ensuring that the pressure on the outside of the pump is equal to the hydrostatic pressure due to the column of fluid in the tubing above the pump to the surface. This characteristic balances pressure spikes on the inside of the pump caused by fluid or gas pound. The discharge of fluid from this pump is at a stationary point at the top of the pump, located the length of the pump away from the bottom hold-down. This characteristic is the trade-off for this type of pump since this stagnant fluid area can lead to corrosion of the outside of the pump barrel or allow sand or other particulates to build up and stick the pump in the tubing.

11AX-0002
11B-0002

◎ZOOM◎

Privacy | Legal

http://www.hfpumps.com/s_api_a.html   1/5/2010

HARBISON-FISCHER MFG. CO.

Featured Product   Employee Login   Related Links   Search   Home

Solutions : API Insert and Tubing Pumps : **Top Hold-Down Insert Pumps**

Product Catalog

Solutions

Support

Sales Locator

Company Info

Success Stories

Contact

Top Hold-Down Insert Pumps, Thin Wall (RWA) and Heavy Wall (RHA)

The Harbison-Fischer API style Top Hold-Down Pump is popular in areas that produce sand or other particulates that tend to accumulate over the hold-down of a Bottom Hold-Down. The fluid discharge point of the Top Hold-Down Pump is only inches away from the location of the hold-down, making it difficult to stick it in the tubing. Other advantages are that the Top Hold-Down Pump has greater fluid submergence than the Bottom Hold-Down Pump and there is not a stagnant fluid area between the hold-down and the fluid discharge point. The Top Hold-Down Pump is not as rugged as the bottom hold-down since the outside of the pump is only subjected to formation pressure.

11AK-0002
11B-0002

Q ZOOM Q

Traveling Barrel Insert Pumps, Thin Wall (RWT) and Heavy Wall (RHT)   Page 1 of 1

Diagram "E"

HARBISON-FISCHER MFG. CO.

"BEST PUMPS IN THE OIL PATCH"

Featured Product | Employee Login | Related Links | Search | Home

Solutions : API Insert and Tubing Pumps : **Traveling Barrel Insert Pumps**

Product Catalog
Solutions
Support
Sales Locator
Company Info
Success Stories
Contact

Traveling Barrel Insert Pumps, Thin Wall (RWT) and Heavy Wall (RHT)

The Harbison-Fischer API style Traveling Barrel Pump is useful in pumping conditions that are characterized by relatively heavy particulate production. The traveling barrel helps to keep sand or other particulates in movement above the hold-down, located on the bottom of the pump, reducing the possibility of a stuck pump. The traveling valve is located on the top of the pump so that it automatically closes in times of pump inactivity, preventing particulates from settling inside the pump. The trade-off for this advantage is that the pump is not as good for gas compression as the two stationary barrel insert pumps, and that the pumping pressure is balanced on a pull tube that can bow and cause extra pump friction and wear on the pull tube.

11AX-0002
11B-0002

ⵔ ZOOM ⵔ

Privacy | Legal

TERRY W. PIESKER

Diagram "F"

HARBISON-FISCHER MFG. CO.

Featured Product | Employee Login | Related Links | Search | Home

Solutions : API Insert and Tubing Pumps : **API Tubing Pumps**

Product Catalog ▸
Solutions ▸
Support ▸
Sales Locator ▸
Company Info ▸
Success Stories
Contact

API Tubing Pumps (TH)

The Harbison-Fischer Tubing Pump is the most rugged of the four API pumps due to its heavy wall construction. It should be chosen when greater production is needed than can be delivered by an insert pump.

The extensions on each end of the barrel provide a stroke-through arrangement. The stroke length and pump spacing can be adjusted so that the plunger strokes out of the barrel into the extensions at the top of the upstroke and bottom of the downstroke. This spacing allows the plunger to be washed clean in the extensions on the upstroke and downstroke.

Although it can produce the greatest quantity of fluid for a particular tubing size, only the plunger assembly and standing valve can be retrieved with the sucker rods for servicing. The tubing must be pulled to service the pump barrel.

11AX-0002
11B-0002

ZOOM

Privacy | Legal

Copyright 2001 Harbison-Fischer Mfg. Co.
All rights reserved

http://www.hfpumps.com/s_api_d.html   1/5/2010

130

10

Repairs and Maintenance

No matter how good your equipment is, you are always going to have repairs and maintenance that needs to be done. Many oil and gas wells in this area are over 25 to 50 years old. Things wear out or need replaced, whether it's pumping units, motors, rods and tubing, pumps, lead lines, tanks, or other things such as these. People are hired to do these various repairs.

Let me start with roustabouts. These are what we call the people who do these various jobs in the oil patch. They lay and repair lead lines, They set and repair pumping units and tank batteries. These people are jacks of all traits. Roustabouts take care of all repairs on above ground equipment. Anything and everything can and will happen. You can have holes in tanks, lead line leaks, motors that go bad, or repair bearings and replace units. Units need to be greased regularly. Pumpers use to do this, but with the contract pumpers having so many wells nowadays, this has become a job that needs to be done by a roustabout crew.

Next we have water trucks. They are used to haul salt water from wells to disposal wells. They haul salt water for workovers and freshwater for squeeze jobs. You need freshwater when using cement. These water trucks are owned by companies where this is basically their only job, to haul water. Most of these companies own several trucks just for this type of job. They pick up many types of fluids, such as oil spills from tanks or lead line leaks.

One of the most important parts of maintenance is chemicals. We deal with highly corrosive salt water downhole. When you have more than one zone open in a well, oftentimes the waters, when commingled, do not mix well. They have a tendency to eat metals or form scale. Chemical companies specialize in chemical only, for battling these types of problems. They have scale inhibitors and corrosion inhibitors to combat these types of problems. They can either be used continuously, with a pumping system that pumps a small amount of chemical down the backside of the well continuously, or the well can be circulated for a few hours once a week or so, depending on how bad the problem really is. Chemical men catch water samples and analysis them in their labs to get the right chemical product in each well. In addition, due to the fact that we have such extreme fluctuations in gravity, from 40 for light oil, to 16 for heavy oil, they have solvents and inhibitors to help break the oil out from the water. These chemicals can be pumped right into the lead lines and start breaking out the oil before it even gets to the gun barrel or separator. Chemicals are very important to the maintenance of an oil well. Without these types of chemical you will be repairing your downhole equipment full time. Chemical is not cheap, but in the long run, they will save you lots of money if used correctly.

Originally, when chemical was first started, the pumper would circulate the chemical down the backside for a few hours and come back by the well and put them back down the lead line, as I mentioned in the pumper chapter, when we had mostly company pumpers. Now a days, with contract pumpers mainly, we have come up with a new method called truck treating, where a truck owned by the chemical company comes by and dumps a few gallons of chemical down the backside of the well and follows with about 10 barrels of lease water as a flush. This is fine on a well that is pumped off, but on high fluid wells, I don't recommend this. The whole purpose of the chemical is to coat the casing, tubing, and rods with a light film of chemical. This can happen on a well that has no extra fluid in the hole, but probably not on a well that has a high fluid level.

The last, and probably the most important part of maintenance and repairs to downhole equipment, is the pulling unit. Pulling units are what pulls the tubing and rods out of the hole. Pulling units come in two sizes, single drums and double drums. The single drum has only one drum called a tubing drum. The double drum has two drums, a tubing drum and a sand line drum. Diagram A depicts a double drum unit. Single drums are becoming extinct because all they can do is pull and run equipment in or out of the hole, where the double drum can swab tubing and casing and clean out the hole with a sand pump or Bailer. A picture of a sand pump and Bailer are in diagram B with an explanation of how they work. Most of the rigs in our area are pole-type rigs. There are also derrick-type rigs for deeper-hole country. Depending on the height of the derrick, these can be single-doubles, which hold 1 joint of tubing and 2 rods, double-doubles, which hold 2 joints of tubing and 2 rods, or double-triples, which hold 2 joints of tubing and 3 rods. In Kansas, all of these types of rigs are truck mounted. They are very mobile. The pulling units, whether single drums or double drums, are manned by 3 man crews, an operator and 2 floor hands. This is a simple explanation of the pulling unit, but you should be able to get the idea.

In addition to these types of maintenance and repair, there are other specialized jobs that should be mentioned. There are pipe testers, who pressure every joint to make sure each joint is capable of handling pressure. This is one of the toughest jobs in the patch, as far as I'm concerned. Say you have a tubing leak in a well. You call a pulling unit and pull rods, pump, and tubing. The tubing is then pressured up to 6,000# on each joint. Often times you will blow a joint out before it gets to that pressure. You will find holes in joints. This way, when the tubing is run back in the hole, you know it will hold. You have eliminated the weak and bad joints. Also, every time you pull a pump, it should be serviced and repaired to make sure all the components of the pump are good and workable.

Another specialized service is the mud pump and swivel. After you have squeezed a well, you have cement about 100' above the leak.

This cement has to be drilled out before you can put the well back on production. You run the bit in the hole on tubing and drill the cement out. To do this, you need to have something to tie on to the top of the tubing once you get to the cement with the bit. This is the swivel. This swivel rotates the tubing and bit as you drill the cement. The mud pump pumps fluid either down the backside or down the tubing, and the returns, the drilled up cement, is circulated to the surface into a pit. Once the cement has been drilled out, the squeezed is tested by pressuring the casing and tubing to a certain point and let set for a few minutes to make sure that the squeeze holds. Sometimes the pulling unit companies will own these mud pumps and swivels and sometimes these units are owned by companies who specialize in only this type of business.

Oftentimes, when you pull into a well, the rods will be parted. You pull the rods out of the hole and one of the rods, a 25' rod, will be broken. You will only come out with part of the rod string. How do you get the rest of the rods out of the hole? You run the rods back in with a fishing tool on bottom and grab hold of the rest of the string. These tools are usually slip-type devices that slip over the broken part of the rod and friction tightens up against the slips so that the broken rod cannot come out. You then pull the rest of the rods and replace the rod and run them back in and put the well back on the pump. Sometimes the tubing will be parted and you pull the rods and if it is an insert pump, you pull it out. You then pull the tubing. You will get the top part of the tubing string. You then run a fishing tool to get hold of the rest of the tubing. With tubing, there are two ways to get it out. You can run an overshot, that goes over the outside of the tubing and has slips, just like fishing rods, or you can run a spear that goes inside the tubing. This spear has slips that work the same way except you go inside the tubing. Either one of these will work. There are other types of tools for fishing rods and tubing, depending on what you have looking up at you on the top of the fish. You may have a rod box that has parted. A rod box is the connecting device that holds one rod to another. In this case, you have to use a different sized overshot. There are companies that specialize in these types of tools. You cannot even imagine all the devices we have to fish different things. I could spend days just discussing this topic.

Repairs and maintenance employs many people in specialized fields. These types of businesses are very important to this industry. Without them, our cost of production would be much higher. No matter how much you do, there will always be problems that develop. As a production foreman, you very seldom get a call with good news. Most of your calls will be problems. You are a trouble shooter.

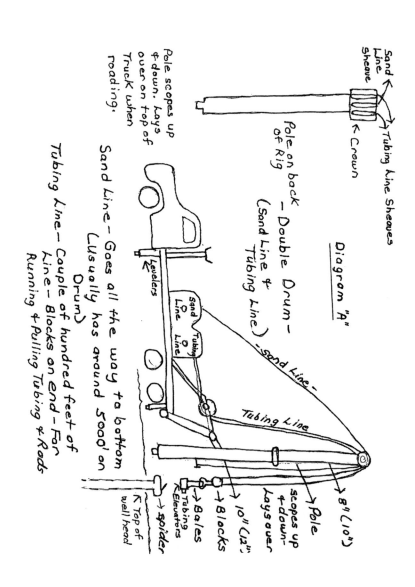

Diagram "A"

Sand Line
Sheave

→ Tubing Line Sheaves

← Crown

Pole on back
of Rig
— Double Drum —
(Sand Line &
Tubing Line)

Pole scopes up
& down. Lays
over on top of
Truck when
roading.

Sand Line— Goes all the way to bottom
(Usually has around 5000' on
Drum)

Tubing Line— Couple of hundred feet of
Line— Blocks on end— For
Running & Pulling Tubing & Rods

Sand Line—

Levelers

Sand
Line

Tubing
Line

Tubing Line

Pole
scopes up
& down-
Lays over

8" (10")

10" (12")

→ Blocks

→ Bales

Tubing
Elevators

→ Spider

← Top of
well head

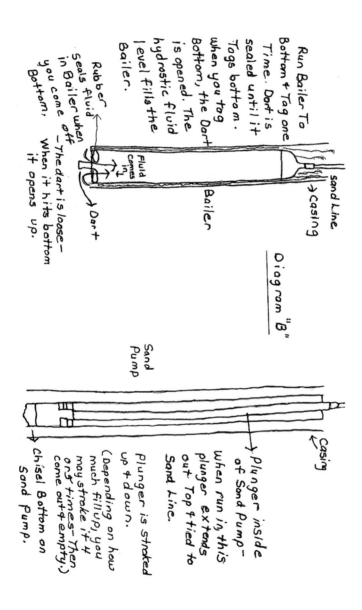

Run Bailer To
Bottom & Tag one
Time. Dart is
sealed until it
Tags bottom.
When you tag
Bottom, the Dart
is opened. The
hydrostic fluid
level fills the
Bailer.

Rubber
Seals fluid
in Bailer when
you come off
Bottom. — The dart is loose —
When it hits bottom
it opens up.

sand Line

→ Casing

Fluid comes in.

→ Dart

Bailer

Diagram "B"

Sand
Pump

← Casing

→ Plunger inside
of Sand Pump —
when run in this
plunger extends
out Top & tied to
Sand Line.

Plunger is stroked
up & down.

(Depending on how
much fill up, you
may stroke it 4
or 5 times — Then
come out & empty.)

chisel Bottom on
Sand Pump.

137

11

GAS WELLS

Drilling for gas wells is no different from drilling for oil wells. The drilling process is exactly the same. One thing that might be different in the drilling, especially when it comes to overpressured areas, is the fact that it might take more mud weight to control the well. In other words, the weight of the drilling fluid will hold the gas back so that it will not flow. When drilling in overpressured reservoirs, it is best to have a blowout preventer on top the surface casing. This blowout preventer (BOP) is for cases where the well might kick off and you lose control. In most places in Kansas this is not a problem, since most of our drilling is done in under pressured reservoirs, reservoirs that will not flow on their own. The blowout preventer is located on top of the surface pipe, below the drilling floor of the drilling rig. There are several types of BOPs. Blind rams, which can be controlled automatically from inside the doghouse, are probably the most common. I have seen manual BOPs that can be opened and closed by manually turning a wheel, much like a gate valve. These are definitely not the safest type of BOPs. These valves should be checked every day when you are drilling the well, to make sure that they will work properly when needed. Obviously, these did not work when we had the BP disaster off the coast of New Orleans a few years ago. However, I don't think that was the only problem they had.

Once you have the well drilled and the casing set, you are now ready to complete the gas well. Depending on what kind of bottom-hole pressure your well has, there are several ways of completing the well. In the old days, we would complete them right down the casing. We would swab the casing down to a point, leaving a certain amount of fluid above where we were going to perforate. You would run your gun in on a wire line and you had a 4 1/2" or 5 1/2" orbit valve on the top of your production casing. You would tie a lubricator on to the orbit valve. This lubricator is a partial joint of casing with a hammer union on the bottom that could be tied into the top of the orbit valve. This lubricator is at least 1' longer than your gun and collar locator so that it will all fit inside the lubricator. The lubricator has a packer off in the top of it so that it will seal off. The wireline on the logging truck goes in the top of the lubricator and then the collar locator and the gun. The gun is all loaded and hooked to the wire line and the gun and lubricator is picked up and tied into the orbit valve on the top of the well. The gun is then run down to spot where you are going to perforate. The pack off on the top of the lubricator is pumped up and the gun is detonated. Once the gun goes off, if you have a really good gas well, the casing will start pressuring up. The lubricator usually has a 2" nipple with a valve on it so you can blow down the lubricator once you have the gun to surface and inside the lubricator. You slowly start out of the hole and bring the gun that you shot back up inside the lubricator and close the orbit valve. Once you have the gun in the lubricator and the orbit valve closed, you have the well under control. You can now open the 2" blow down valve and dismantle the lubricator and the gun.

Remember one thing with a gas well, especially an overpressured gas well, don't take any chances that the well could get away from you. Always error on the side of caution. If you think there is any chance at all of the well getting away from you, do whatever it takes to be safe. I have seen 1,000# to 1,200# on these lubricators before the gun got back to surface. Without a lubricator and orbit valve on the well, you would be in trouble. Those kind of pressures are no fun to play with. Sometimes you end up having nothing after you have shot the zone.

This is all right, but you want to make sure that you keep the controls on the well because it could come at you at any time. Now you will run tubing and packer and probably treat the well. Once you have treated the well, you will swab it down and test it. You can test the well through orifice plates with different size holes or through a choke that is calibrated for different size holes. The amount of pressure build up and the size of the orifice will tell you what kind of volume you are producing. Gas is measured in cubic feet. It is sold in 1,000 cubic feet volumes. 5 MCFs is 5,000 cubic feet.

A second way to perforate the well is to run what we call a tubing conveyed gun. This type of perforating is done with the tubing in the hole. You run the gun right on the tubing. You run the gun and tubing in the hole with the gun on the bottom of the tubing. Once you get the gun in the hole with a seating nipple above the gun, you get a logging truck to run in with a collar locator and tie into the casing collars and position the gun right where you want to perforate. Once this has been done, you seal the tubing head and put an orbit valve on the tubing. Now you can drop a rod down the tubing that will set the perforating gun off when it hits bottom. You have already swabbed the well down dry so, if the well is any good, you should have gas to surface almost immediately in this well. You can get a pressure truck out and pump water down the casing or tubing and kill the well so that it no longer flows. One thing to keep in mind, you always need something to control the well in case it kicks off. You do not want the well to get away from you. The good part about most of Kansas is the fact that we are dealing with under pressured reservoirs that are fairly easy to control. When you're dealing with overpressured reservoirs, they are a whole different animal.

The second difference is the hook up on the surface. Once you have the gas well completed and shut in with an orbit valve on your tubing, you need to put in the support system to get gas to the pipeline company. If you have a good gas well, you will need a gas pack unit. This will be your controlling device for controlling the flow of gas to the pipeline. We use what we call minipacks. Attached is diagram A, which depicts a minipack unit. This unit comes right off the well head of the gas well. The gas flows through the pack, which has a heater and a water bath to warm the gas. The line winds around inside the pack to warm the gas up. As the gas goes out the pack, it is run through a choke, which controls the volume. By twisting the wheel on the choke, the flow is lowered, thus the pressure builds behind the choke, inside the vessel. Choke sizes range from 1/64th inch up to about 2". Depending on how much gas you want to move down the line, you can set the choke on that size. As you run this gas through the choke, the temperature change has a tendency to make liquids. These liquids need to be taken out of the gas. To sell gas into a pipe line, it has to be dry. Thus, you need a vessel to knock the water out of the gas. Gas is very light. Thus, the flow of gas goes into a separator in the bottom and the water drops out as the gas goes to the top of the vessel. At the bottom of the vessel is a float that lets the water go to a tank. This float controls the flow of water out of the vessel and the dry gas then goes through a meter run and then down the pipe line. The meter gauges the amount of gas going into the pipe line. This is what you are paid off of. Attached is diagram B, which depicts the whole system. This is just a general idea of how the system is set up. There can be many different types of hook ups, but this will just give you some idea.

Most of the gas wells in Kansas are much lower pressure than mentioned above. Many of the gas wells that I have completed were very low pressure and made some water. In this case, most of these wells were on the pump, making water up the tubing and gas was being produced from the annulus. These types of wells are much easier to control on completion and when putting on production. One thing about gas wells, always be safe and do overkill when it comes to completion. It's always better to be safe than sorry.

As I mentioned above, gas is sold in 1,000 cubic feet increments. In addition, gas has what we call a Btu value. Btu stands for British thermal units. The definition of Btu is the amount of energy needed to heat one pound of water by one degree Fahrenheit. This doesn't mean a whole lot to me, so this just gives you some idea how gas is sold. Several years ago, you could get rid of gas that was below 1,000 Btu. In other words, you could sell gas with a value of say 800 to 850 Btu. The value of this type of gas was based on 1,000 Btu and the price that you would get was 80% to 85% of the price. The value of 1 MCF was based on 1,000 Btu and you would get the percentage of price if the Btu value of your gas was below 1,000 Btu. Today this is not the case. A pipeline will not take gas unless it is 1,000 Btu or higher. How do you get the gas up to 1,000 Btu? You start stripping things out of the gas. For example, you can take the Nitrogen out of the gas. This can raise your Btu value quite a bit. You can extract the helium out of the gas. Helium is quite valuable. There is a market for helium. You can sell helium. As a matter of fact, the helium price is quite a bit more than the value of butane, methane, and propane. There are other gases that can be extracted to get your Btu value up to the 1,000 Btu mark. This all costs money. There is a point where this extraction is cost prohibitive. It becomes uneconomical to produce. A lot of the gas in Kansas is 500 to 850 Btu. We always use to say that gas had to be above 750 Btu in order for it to burn.

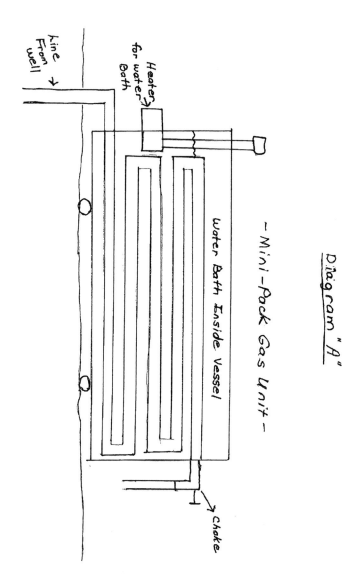

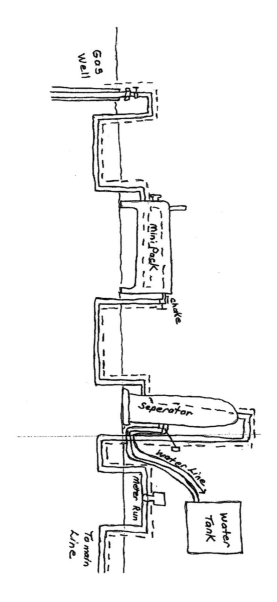

Diagram "B"

Surface Setup for Gas Well

12

WORKOVERS

Every once in a while you have to go back in on a well, whether it's a casing leak, a clean out job, to retreat zones, or open new zones. In addition, I have a chapter, later in this book, on one of the more exotic completions or workovers, the frac job. Everything I talked about in the completion section can be done as a workover, such as isolating zones separately, limited entry work, and the acid plug job.

First, let's look at the casing leak. You now have a hole in the casing that is causing you some kind of problem, either water has broken in, or your equipment is being eaten up. In Kansas, we have a very corrosive water-bearing zone called the Dakota, which causes all sorts of problems. In certain places, this is like an underground river. It can cut casing just like a Torch. If it has not been cemented off properly, you can have a casing leak with in 6 months of drilling the well. We also have a salt section that can cause problems too. Over the years, it is only understandable that the casing will wear out. We have wells that are 50 to 60 years old. Almost all of these have had a casing leak at one time or another. Usually, the repair of these are pretty simple. First off all, you pull all the equipment out of the hole. Test the tubing and replace all bad joints. You then run a retrievable bridge plug with a packer right above it. You run this in on your tubing. You set the plug above any producing formation, but hopefully clear down where you have good cement on the outside of your casing. Once you have the plug set and you have gotten off the plug, you pull one joint out of the hole and set the packer, which will be on the end of the tubing. Now you load the tubing and pressure up on the plug. You should pressure up on the plug to whatever pressure you plan on squeezing the well. Usually this will be 1,500# to 2,000#. This way you know that your plug is secure. Not knowing for sure that you have a leak, I would tie to the backside and see if you can pump into the hole. Usually I would not go over 500# while doing this, so that I do not make more holes. Once you have decided that you have a leak, you would release the packer and spot about 2 sacks of sand on top of the bridge plug. You do this by mixing sand with water and pumping it down to bottom by volume. Now you have to give it a little time for the sand to settle out. Once this has been done, you start moving up the hole by setting the packer every so often, and pressuring down the tubing to see if it holds. You can also go down the backside, but you would not want to use as much pressure on that side. You need to locate the hole, usually within one joint. Lots of times you find out that you have more than one hole. Usually, depending on how close and how much distance you have, you can squeeze them all at once. Other times you might find out that they are communicated. By communicated, I mean that when you set the packer between them, water is pumped around the packer on the outside of the pipe and back inside the casing through the top hole. Usually these can be squeezed together at the same time. Once in a while you will get holes that at 500' to 600' apart and are not communicated. You would squeeze the bottom hole and move up and squeeze the top hole. This would entail setting the packer between the two holes and squeezing the bottom hole first and then releasing the packer and coming up and squeezing the top hole. This can be extremely dangerous because you cannot keep the backside loaded to monitor if cement might be coming around. If cement comes around, and you don't know it, it will come around and set right on top of you packer. This is not good. When you try to released the packer it will not come out of the hole. You are stuck. This is a costly mistake. Now back to a normal squeeze. Once you have the hole located, you would take an injection rate at so many barrels per minute at such and such a pressure. Let's say you have a hole that will take 2 barrels per minute (bpm) at 250. This is pretty loose. We are going to squeeze this with cement. In other words, we are going to squeeze cement out this hole and basically put a patch on it. Once you have done this for a while, you will know roughly how much cement you will need to get this done. Until that time, you should rely on the cementing company man to give you some idea what he thinks. Usually this would probably take 150 to 200 sacks of cement. Next, depending on how deep the squeeze is, you can put additives into the cement that accelerate the setting time. Calcium chloride (CC) is a great accelerator. If the hole is fairly high, I would recommend using CC. If the hole is low, you probably won't have too, since temperature is an excellent accelerator. The bottom-hole temperature at 3,500' is somewhere around 100 to 105 Degrees. Now up the hole, the temperature is much lower. First of all, you would move the packer up about 100' above the top hole and set the packer. Load the backside and put about 300# to 500# on it and shut it in so that you can watch it. This is very important. Now you start pumping down the tubing at the rate you established. Start mixing your cement while keeping a close eye on the pressure as the cement gets on bottom. You know when the cement gets close to bottom because you know how many barrels it takes to get the cement to bottom. Also, you need to keep an eye on the backside pressure and make sure it does not come up. It probably will not stay exactly the same as what you put on it, but you'll know if it is coming around once cement hits bottom. While you are pumping, you do not want to see the backside climbing as the pressure on the tubing climbs. In other words, if the two pressures seem to be the same for a long period of time, you probably have a problem. Once again, you do not want cement on top of your packer. If this happens, you need to immediately release the packer and circulate the hole clean and start over. You have a big problem, but nothing like what you have if you leave it in the hole. Once you have all the cement mixed, you have figured, and so has the cementer, exactly what it takes, volume wise, to get to the top hole. You also have a volume number for what it takes to get to the packer. The cement company will break off from the well and clean out the pump and lines and tie back on to the tubing. You now begin your displacement. Depending on what you are squeezing, and what your pressure was when you shut down, will determine how quickly you want to get the cement out of the tubing and below the packer. If you set 100' above the top hole in 5 1/2" casing, you have 2.5 bbl below the packer. You do not want to pump past the hole. You need to keep a little cement on top, at least a barrel. Hopefully, by the time you get to the packer, you have 500# to 1,000# on it. Before you started this job, you had some idea what you wanted to squeeze the well to, say 1,200# to 2,000#. If all is working as you planned, you are pumping somewhere around 800# and you are down to 1/2 bbl per minute and you have maybe 1 bbl of cement left in your tubing and the 2.5 bbl below the packer. You shut the pump down and it shuts in at 500#. You now are beginning the squeeze. Remember, it takes time for the cement to set up. It shut down at 500# and after 5 minutes it had dropped to 300#. You have dropped your pumping rate down. You might let it set for 15 minutes and pump on it again. We call this stagging. You pump another 1/2 bbl into the well, and you now have 1,000#, and it shut down at 800#. Remember, you still have 1/2 bbl of cement in the tubing. Let it set another 5 minutes and pump the other 1/2 bbl out. You are now almost clear of the end of the tubing. The pressure went to 1,000# and broke back to 800# while you were pumping. You shut it in and it went to 500#. You watched it for 15 minutes and it came down to 400#. Pump another 1/2 bbl, and it walks up to 1,200# and shuts in at 1,000#. You are in good shape now because you are 1/2 bbl past the end of the packer. You can feel a little more at ease since you have the cement out the tubing and past the packer. Now time becomes your friend. You have two more barrels to get to the top perforation, so you have about 1 bbl to play with. You let it set another 15 minutes and you pump on it and it immediately goes to 1,500#. It holds solid for 5 minutes. You should be done. You now release the pressure back into the truck and watch and make sure that the fluid dies to nothing. If it does, you have the well squeezed. You release the pressure on the backside. You then release the packer and circulate the hole clean to make sure you have no cement around your packer or in the tubing. Once you have that done, you can pull a joint and reset the packer and pressure up to make sure it is holding. You can stay on this as long as you want. You then release the packer and pull the tubing and packer. As in all jobs, when you are young and new, pay attention to all service companies. They can teach you a lot. These are usually very experienced and knowledgeable people in their particular field. They are the experts at what they do. They do the same thing every day. Once you have the well squeezed, you run a bit and drill out the cement. Pressure the casing, tubing, and bit to 500# and make sure your squeeze holds. If it does, you go down and wash the sand off the plug and pull the tubing and bit. You then run in with the bridge plug catcher on tubing and release the plug and pull tubing and plug. Often times I swab the well down to a certain depth once the catcher and tubing have been run to the plug, before it is released. I don't like to put additional pressure on the producing reservoir. It really depends what I am producing from. Once the plug is out of the hole, you are ready to run it in and put it back on production.

Just a few things about the squeeze job. It can be done with a permanent plug, which we call a cast iron bridge plug (CIBP). This type of plug is set on a wire line truck (perforating company). This might be done when you think all your pipe might be bad, or when you think you might have a chance to not get a retrievable bridge plug back out of the hole. Say for example, the holes in the pipe might be really close to the only place you can set a bridge plug.

Also, lots of people wash out the cement after the job. By this I mean, once they have gotten the squeeze done and it holds, they run tubing down and wash out the cement clear below the perforations or holes. This way they do not have to drill the cement out. I would never do this. I like to do a job only once. When you do this you are asking for trouble. At least 50% of the time it will not hold. Another time you might have to squeeze is when you open up a zone that you thought would be productive and it turns out to make water. You would basically go in and do exactly the same thing. You just shut the water off. Usually any type of squeeze job will hold for several years, depending on what you are squeezing.

Now say that you had a well that you originally completed in the Arbuckle or a lower zone in the L-KC. You also had a DST in the Upper L-KC that you chose not to open at the time of completion. After producing the original zones for a few years, you have depleted them. Let's say they are down to 5 BOPD and about 10 BWPD. You have a test in the A zone that you think should be productive. You pull rods, pump, and tubing. I would recommend that the tubing be tested while it is out of the hole. You have decided where you want to shoot the A zone. You would call a perforating company and get them out on location and perforate the A zone. Once it has been perforated, you would run a retrievable bridge plug and packer on your tubing. The bridge plug will be used to keep the existing zones from being touched. In other words, you would set the bridge plug above your existing zones and set your packer above your new zone, thus isolating the A zone. The bridge plug has a J Slot catcher that runs on the bottom of your packer. You set the bridge plug and then get off of it. The rest of the workover would be done just like your completion. You treat the zone and test. When you are finished with the work, and you have what you thought you should have, you release the packer and go down and get back on the bridge plug and release it. You then pull the tubing, packer, and bridge plug and run the well back in and put on production. This is pretty simple. If you wanted to retreat a zone, you simply isolate it and do the same thing.

Oftentimes, when you are completing zones that are close together, the cement between the zones on the outside of the pipe will give way and you will communicate. You now have a problem. How do you get these zones treated? You have a good idea that they are both productive. You had your plug set below the bottom zone and your packer set above one of the zones and below the top zone. In other words, you had the bottom zone isolated. You made a pull with the tubing swab and you were watching the annulus (area between the 5 1/2" casing and the tubing), and as you came off bottom with the swab, it began to suck. We usually have a rag or baggie on the backside so that we can tell if the zone communicates up. It is wise to do this even if you don't have a zone above you, just to make sure you don't have a tubing leak or a bad packer. Once you have determined that your zones are truly communicated, you can release your packer and raise it above the top zone. I would probably test them together and determine how much acid I would like to give them. I would treat this well at a fairly good rate if I had some decent oil, and not much water. If, after treating the well and testing it, I felt that I did not get into both zones, I could do what we call an acid plug job, as I mentioned in the Completion Chapter, previously.

Another possibility, if you have communications, is to squeeze the zones and start over. This will usually depend on how much room you have between the zones that communicated. If you have 30' to 50' between zones, this would probably not be a bad idea. If they are 8' to 10' apart, you may be wasting your time and money. One thing to remember, once you have squeezed the zones off, it may take a lot more pressure to get back into them than it would normally take, depending on how much cement went back into the zone. Remember, your perforations, which you will have to do again, will only go back about 30" to 39". Hopefully you can get back far enough to get these opened once you have squeezed them off.

Now let me explain the cleaning out of an old well. Over the years, these wells will fill up with iron sulfide on bottom. This happens quite often when different zones are commingled. Usually waters from different zones are not very compatible. Iron sulfide usually results in the mixture of different waters. Chemicals will help this for a while, but over time it will still build up and shut off the zones.

The first thing you do is lay the well out, which means you pull the rods, pump, and tubing. Next, you have several choices. First, you could run a sand pump. This would be the quickest thing you could do. The sand pump would be run on the sand line of a double drum work-over rig. It would be run down the inside of the casing to the bottom of the well. Once you get on bottom, it has a plunger inside of it that you work up and down to suck the iron sulfide up in the barrel of the sand pump. It has a stroke length, depending on the size, of 10 to 20 feet. You stroke the pump 4 or 5 times and come out of the hole with the pump. You have a flapper on the bottom of the pump, so that once you start out of the hole, the trash off bottom will stay up inside the sand pump itself. You can see a diagram of this in the maintenance chapter.

Secondly, you can run a bit on tubing and go down to bottom and drill out the hole to the original rotary total depth or the plug back total depth, provided you can get circulation to the surface. This would be a lot like drilling the well, except you are using smaller equipment which fits inside your casing. For 5 ½" casing, the bit would be 4 7/8" on 2 3/8" or 2 7/8" tubing, and for 4 ½" casing this would be a 3 7/8" bit on 2 3/8" tubing. Usually you can use water to drill with. You will need a mud pump and a power swivel. The mud pump will pump the fluid down the hole and around the bottom and back up to surface. The swivel will turn the tubing to make hole. You can go either way with the mud pump; either down the tubing and up the casing, which we call the long way, or down the casing and up the tubing, which we call the short way, because all it takes to get bottoms up the short way is the volume inside the tubing which is much less then the long way. All you do is drill down to bottom and circulate the hole clean. Once you have this done, you can swab the hole down and test, or spot acid and treat to clean up.

Now, what if the hole will not load? This would happen if you had low pressure zones. In other words, you could not pump enough water to get fluid to the surface. Your producing zones would take all the water you could pump to them. You could run what we call a bull dog bailer. This runs basically on the same principle as the sand pump, except you run this on tubing. You need to know a little about your well. You need to know your standing fluid level in the well. Once you know that, you can figure out where you want to put your pump. The pump must be in fluid to work correctly. It is also nice to know how much fill up you have to clean out. You can usually get some idea by running a sand pump to bottom. This will give you an idea where fluid is and also how much fill up you might have in the bottom. Once you have these two bits of information, you can figure out where you want to run the pump and how much cavity you will need to clean out that much hole. This can all be figured fairly closely. So you run a bit on the bottom of your tubing and a flapper assembly to hold the cuttings up inside the tubing. You have figured you have about 50' of hole to clean out and your fluid level is 800' off bottom. You are using 2 7/8" tubing- which is also called 2 ½" tubing. To clean out about 100' of hole you would need about 400' of cavity. So you run 400' of tubing (the inside of the tubing is the cavity) above the bit and put your pump on top of this, about 400' off bottom. The pump is about 12' long with a 6' stroke length. Right on top of this you would run a 4' perforated sub. Now you just run the rest of the tubing until you get to bottom. Once you get to bottom you would stroke the pump 2 or 3 times to clean up anything loose. You will now need a swivel to turn your tubing. You tie the swivel on to the tubing and begin drilling and going down hole about 2'. Once you have made the 2', you stroke the pump to pick up all the cuttings of what you have just drilled. You do this in 2' intervals all the way down to your TD. Once you have the hole cleaned out to TD, you start out of the hole with the tubing. You will be fine until you get to the pump. From here on down, every joint will be full of fluid and cuttings. It is a nasty job, but the hole is clean. From here, you can run a packer on tubing and treat the zone and test.

This gives you some idea of what you can do with a few different situations. In this business lots of things come up over the course of time. Sometimes you just have to use your head and try to figure out what would be the best for each particular well. This all comes with experience. Use your service companies for help. Remember, they are the real experts in whatever their field is, such as logging, cementing, acidizing, and so on.

13

GAS AND WATER DRIVEN RESERVOIRS, WATERFLOODING, AND SALT WATER DISPOSAL WELLS

In Kansas, we have lots of zones that are primarily gas driven. What this means is the driving force behind getting oil to the well bore is gas. As I mentioned earlier, the Lansing-Kansas City has eleven or twelve distinctly different zones. Each zone is separated by shale, and depending on how good a cement job you have in the well, they can all be produced individually. The majority of these zones are gas driven, or maybe they will produce a small amount of water. What happens is this, after they have produced for a few years, the gas has been taken out of the reservoir, thus the bottom-hole pressure (BHP) has been depleted. The production that has been produced to this point is called primary production.

Let me explain exactly how all this works. Scientifically, engineers can figure out how many barrels of oil are in place in a specific zone. You see, oil is not like a lake. Oil is actually in the pores of the rock. Depending on porosity and permeability of each zone, this number can be calculated. This is way over my head, but engineers and scientists can come up with formulas to calculate the number of barrels of oil in place. An oil well will only produce a small percentage of the total oil in place. This depends on the rocks unique qualities, such as porosity and permeability, and the wells drainage capacity. This number will usually be somewhere between 0 to 40% of the actual oil in place.

In gas driven reservoirs it's very important to keep at least some of this gas captured for as long as possible. In other words, keep some back pressure on the back side of the well. As you produce oil up the inside of the tubing, the gas, which is very light, will come up the backside in the casing. In order to not release the gas through a vent to the atmosphere, you can install a back-pressure valve at the well head, with a vent, so you can keep at least some pressure in the casing. This can be regulated, so not all the gas is let out to the atmosphere. Also, if the well will produce a lot of fluid, you can keep this gas in the formation by keeping a high fluid level, just as you would do in a water driven well. As the fluid decreases, and your gas starts coming out the backside, now you will need the back-pressure valve. If you do things correctly, the cumulative oil recovered will far surpass the cumulative barrels in a well that is gutted from day one.

The second type of reservoir that we have in Kansas is the water driven reservoir. The Arbuckle formation is just such an animal. These types of water driven reservoirs will have a tendency to recover quite a bit more oil than a gas driven reservoir. Over the years of production in the water driven reservoir, the water percentage will tend to climb and the oil percentage will tend to decline, until the well becomes uneconomical to produce. In these types of reservoirs, it is very important to start out slowly with your production. You should definitely keep fluid in the hole and not pump these wells down too fast. These zones usually have decent bottom-hole pressures, so it is best to keep a high fluid level in these types of wells. Once you start pumping these types of wells down, you suck the water into the well bore and you end up coning the well. You will find an example of this in diagram A, which explains how this happens. Remember one thing, you are trying to produce the most amount of oil you can over the life of this well, not the most you can get out of it in one day. I have seen and known people who have gutted this type of well and they were done in a couple of years. If they would have treated the well correctly, they would have produced twice as much oil over three or four times as long.

Now with a water driven well, the water will actually help carry the oil to the well bore. That, in my opinion, is why the recovery on water driven zones will usually far surpass that of gas driven zones. This gives you some idea of the different types of zones.

There are ways to enhance the recovery of both the water driven reservoirs and the gas driven reservoirs. Let me try to mention a few of those.

First the gas driven reservoir. These zones can be enhanced by what we call waterflooding, or secondary recovery. Remember, we call all oil produced to this point, primary oil recovery.

Waterflooding

Waterflooding consists of putting water down a well and pushing the oil to other producing wells. We call these injection wells. We would be injecting water into the same zones that your producing wells are producing from. Attached is a diagram of a waterflood injection well, diagram B. In our area, the Lansing-Kansas City zones are usually the waterflood projects. A field or reservoir is usually drilled out. The locations on these projects are usually around 660' apart. Some of these fields are large, say 20 to 30 wells, while others are very small, say 4 to 10 wells.

These fields are usually small closures that are very well defined with dry holes on or around the edges. You can see this in diagram C. You can think of these closures as balloons.

Water is injected into the injection well. Usually, if this is a designed waterflood, the amount of water that goes in the well is monitored. However, we do have, what we call dump floods, in which water is just put down the well in hopes it improves production. The Theory is that a wall of water pushes the oil out of the porous rocks over to a producing well. This is a slow process that will take usually at least 6 months or more, depending how far the producing wells are from the injection well. At first, these injection wells will take water on their own, or what we would say, on vacuum. As the closure fills up, more then likely, you will have to pump the water into the zone. You will install an injection pump that will pump the water down the well and into the formation. What you are actually doing is rebuilding the bottom-hole pressure in this reservoir that you lost when the gas dropped off. As the water from the injection well starts to move the oil in place to the producing well, your oil production will begin to increase in the producers. At first you will see almost all oil in the producers. It's like a wall of oil moving toward the producers. As time goes on, the oil will tapper off, and you will begin seeing more water at the producing wells. Finally, at the end of the flood, you will begin producing more water than you can handle. Often, at this point, you can shut the injection off and picking up some of the oil that has been pushed past the producers. You will always be leaving some oil in place. The oil that you have produced because of this flooding, is called secondary recovery oil. A part of the oil that has been recovered during this time, depending on what the producers were making before the flood started, will still be called primary oil because even without the flood, this oil would have been produced anyway. Many of these waterflood projects will last 30 to 40 years.

Waterflooding does not work in every area. The only way to really know if it will work is to try it out. Many waterfloods that I have been associated with have recovered several times more oil on secondary recovery than primary recovery.

As I mentioned earlier, it can be calculated, how much oil is in place to begin with. Oftentimes, primary oil in a water driven reservoir will recover 30% to 40%. You will never recover all the oil in place. In a gas driven reservoir, you might recover 10 to 15% of the oil in place with primary recovery and then as much as another 20% to 30% from secondary recovery. Scientist and engineers are always working on processes to raise the recovery of the remaining oil left in place. For the gas driven reservoirs, different types of polymers are being tried, along with various types of gases, such as CO_2. Presently, we are leaving a lot of oil in the ground. Hopefully, some day, we'll develop a process that can recover more and more of this oil left in place.

I have talked about the processes of recovering more oil in the gas driven reservoir. In addition, there are some processes going on with the water driven reservoirs. In the water driven reservoir you don't have the problem of losing your bottom-hole pressure like in the gas driven reservoir. The problem you have is the fact that the oil is overtaken by the water, in a water driven reservoir. It use to be, when the water got too costly to get rid of and the oil depleted down to nothing, all you could do was plug the well. It had reached its economic limit. The economic limit is the point where producing the well, no longer makes a profit. You could go in with bigger equipment, such as a Reda, which will produce 1,500 to 5,000 barrel of fluid per day, or a screw pump, which can do about the same and probably make 1 to 3% oil for a while. Now we are coming up with new processes to shut the water off.

There are presently two methods for this. The first method is an old method called the DOC squeeze. This entails mixing Diesel with common cement and pushing it back in the formation. The theory behind this is that Diesel based cement will only set up in water. Thus, you can shut off some of the water entering the well bore and produce more oil. I have seen this work in some areas.

The second method is a type of polymer. A large amount of polymer is pumped out the perforations and allowed to set up and shut off the water as it tries to get back to the well bore. This is like a net that allows oil to flow through it, but the polymer helps shut off some of the water. The secret here is not to pump the well to hard when you put it back on. Leave a high fluid level in the well so that the polymer is not sucked back out to the well bore.

Both of these work in certain areas, but I have seen them fail too. Presently it is a trial and error process. Hopefully, down the road, we start to understand where and why these processes work. These are both costly processes.

Salt Water–Disposal Wells

Almost every oil or gas well in Kansas produces salt water with the oil or gas. No matter what, this salt water has to be put away somewhere.

Remember, this is not freshwater, it is salt water. In order to get rid of this water, we have to put it back into the ground. We do this with a salt water disposal well.

These wells are very important to the oil business. If you can't get rid of the salt water, then you can't produce all the oil possible. These wells can be as important as the producing wells themselves. These are extremely important to water driven reservoirs, such as the Arbuckle and the Mississippi.

What you have is one specific well that it's only purpose is to get rid of this salt water. The Arbuckle is usually a good zone to put this water back into. You see, the Arbuckle formation is usually 200' to 300' thick. Usually, the only productive sections of the Arbuckle are located within the top 100' of this zone. What we usually do is drill the well at least 100' to 150' into the Arbuckle and then set pipe about 100' into the Arbuckle and leave about 50' of open hole in which to put the disposed water. It is very important that you protect the productive sections of the Arbuckle from this disposed water. You don't want this disposal water coming back out at your producing wells. To protect these producing zones in the Arbuckle, we try to set pipe at least 50' past the last productive section of the zone. Since the Arbuckle is water driven, which means, more than likely it will give up large amounts of water some time during its producing life, then it should also take large amounts of water. In other words, if the well will produce water, it should, in return, take water.

These lower sections of the Arbuckle will usually give up large amounts of water when open. Let me mention one amazing fact about the Arbuckle. When you open up a section of the Arbuckle and you swab, let's say, 20 barrel of water per hour, if you try to inject water into this zone, 95% of the time, it will not go. So how do you get water into the formation? You spot acid on the Arbuckle, which is a dolomite, and all of the sudden it will take water. To have a good disposal, you want the well to take your water on a vacuum. What this means is, the water will go without any force, or pump at the surface. You ask, how can this be? Remember, the well is say 4,000' deep. The bottom-hole pressure is 1,000#, thus the static fluid level, which is where fluid will stand all the time, is about 1,500' from the surface. As I explained in an earlier chapter, hydrostatic pressure comes into play here. The weight of fluid from the surface to this 1,500' level will let the water go into the zone of injection on its own. We call this going on a vacuum. In other words, this weight of fluid will allow the well to take water without any surface pressure. At the surface it will be on a suction. A suction gauge can be put on the well head to monitor this vacuum. These Arbuckle wells will take anywhere from 1 bpm to 20+ bpm, depending on the size of the disposal string in the disposal well. What I mean by a disposal string, is what the fluid is run down through the well to get to the disposal zone. If it is 2 3/8" tubing, this will only take so much fluid per minute before friction pressure restricts the flow. Usually this would be 1.5 to 2 bpm before friction pressure would develop at the surface, where if you had, say 4 1/2" casing for your disposal string, it would probably take up to about 10 bpm before you would see any friction pressure at the surface. The size of the disposal string is dependent on the amount of salt water that you need to get rid of on a daily basis. In other words, the amount of fluid that you will produce and the amount of salt water you will need to get rid of per day, will determine the size of your disposal string.

Since we are dealing with salt water and not freshwater, it is very important that we make sure that we never get the salt water into the freshwater-bearing zones. These zones, the freshwater zones, are always located at the top of the drilled well. In order to prevent these two waters from ever getting together, we must have good protection. In Kansas, the Kansas Corporation Commission (KCC) tries to make sure this does not happen. You see, freshwater is becoming harder and harder to find in our country. It is becoming a valuable commodity. Attached, is exhibit D, a diagram of a salt water disposal well. The KCC requires that there be two layers of protection from the salt water getting to the freshwater, in order for you to get a salt water disposal permit.

Let me explain the two types of protection. First, when you drilled the well, you set surface pipe through all possible freshwater zones. This surface pipe was cemented on the outside with cement from the surface to the bottom of the pipe. Next, after you ran pipe, you either ran a port collar or a DV tool from a certain point below the noncommercial salt water–bearing zones located just below the freshwater zones. In

Kansas this is usually done from the anhydrite to the surface. We have what we call the Dakota zone, which is a very high volume salt water–bearing zone. This is a sand zone that can be 200' to 300' thick, which lies right below the freshwater-bearing zones. In addition, the upper part of the Dakota can be almost fresh. In some areas, this Dakota is almost like a flowing underground river. It can cut through pipe in less than 6 months in some areas. Thus, getting good cement on the outside of your pipe is very important. It is important to the operator and the owner of the Land who probably uses the freshwater. It saves the operator from having to repair the pipe by squeezing the well. Thus, we have two layers of protection, the surface pipe being cemented from top to bottom and the cement behind the production string from a certain area with cement on the backside to protect any salt water from contaminating the freshwater. This is very important!

Now the KCC makes you run a special type of tubing with a packer on bottom of this tubing, which will be set somewhere within 50' of the top of the zone of injection. You can see how this is all set up in diagram D. The tubing that is run into this type of well is lined with a plastic liner. The plastic liner is very important because this salt water can be very corrosive and eat right through the steel tubing. Inserts are installed as you are running each joint so that none of the threads or collars are subjected to the salt water as it is run down through the tubing to the zone of injection. When the well is finally ready to be put in use, the KCC makes the operator run what we call an MIT (mechanical integrity test) to make sure that everything is covered correctly. The annulus between the tubing and casing is filled with chemical and freshwater, so that nothing can eat from the backside of the tubing. This is done by displacing the formation water out of the hole and replacing it with the treated water. Once this has been done, the packer will be set and the annulus between the casing and the tubing will be pressured up to 300#. It has to hold for 30 minutes solid. Once this is done, your permit can be approved, and the well can be used. The KCC monitors this by making you do an MIT every 5 years. If it does not pass the MIT, you have to go in and repair the well, or plug it.

Often times, you will have an old well that you can convert into a salt water disposal well. Sometimes this can be done quite easily, and other times it can be very expensive. It depends how many times you have to squeeze off your old zones or if you have to perforate the upper section of the casing so that you can get cement across the upper sections and circulate to the surface. Sometimes, depending on how old the well is, this could take several squeezes. Also, you don't want to many old holes in your pipe because you still have to pass an MIT. Lots of times, these old squeezes will come loose and that costs money to repair.

If the lease does not have a disposal well, or it's not hooked to a disposal well, the water will have to be trucked off and put into another disposal well. This can become costly, depending on the amount of fluid that the producer or producers make. Thus, you have to decide, is it cheaper to have a disposal, or is cheaper to haul the water off? These are important decisions that have to be made in regards to economics and the life of the well.

Almost every lease in Kansas will be hooked up to a disposal well. These are highly important. In addition, it is very important where the disposal is located in regards to the tank battery. Your disposal needs to be lower than your gun barrel so that the water will run to it without using a pump. This saves money, if at all possible. In this business, we try to save money every way we can. Remember, the oil business is like going to Vegas. You never know till the end if you are a winner.

Diagram "A"

– Coning –

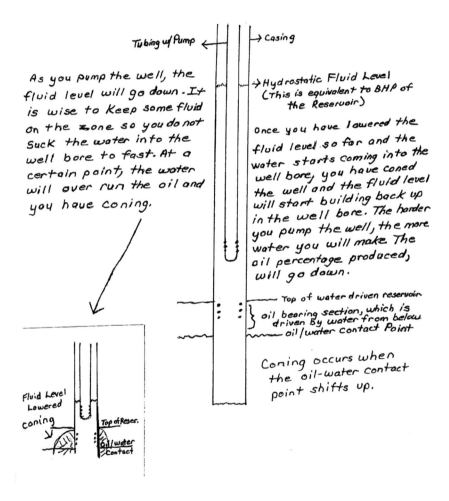

Tubing w/ Pump ←   → Casing

As you pump the well, the fluid level will go down. It is wise to keep some fluid on the zone so you do not suck the water into the well bore to fast. At a certain point, the water will over run the oil and you have coning.

→ Hydrostatic Fluid Level (This is equivalent to BHP of the Reservoir)

Once you have lowered the fluid level so far and the water starts coming into the well bore, you have coned the well and the fluid level will start building back up in the well bore. The harder you pump the well, the more water you will make. The oil percentage produced, will go down.

— Top of water driven reservoir

} oil bearing section, which is driven by water from below

— oil/water contact Point

Coning occurs when the oil-water contact point shifts up.

Fluid Level Lowered

coning

Top of Reser.

Oil/water Contact

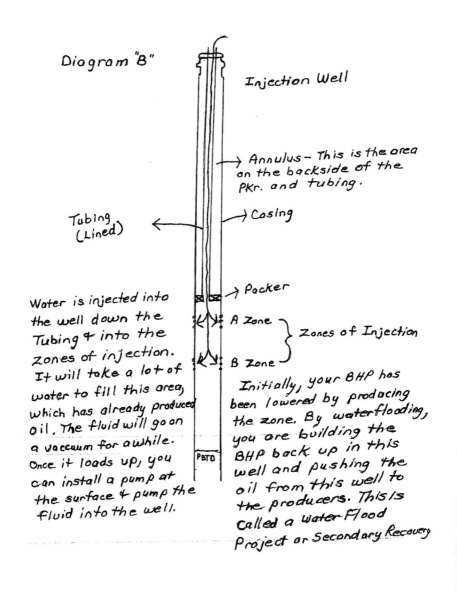

Diagram "B"

Injection Well

→ Annulus - This is the area on the backside of the Pkr. and tubing.

→ Casing

Tubing (Lined) ←

→ Packer

→ A Zone

} Zones of Injection

B Zone

PBTD

Water is injected into the well down the Tubing & into the Zones of injection. It will take a lot of water to fill this area, which has already produced oil. The fluid will go on a vaccuum for awhile. Once it loads up, you can install a pump at the surface & pump the fluid into the well.

Initially, your BHP has been lowered by producing the zone. By waterflooding, you are building the BHP back up in this well and pushing the oil from this well to the producers. This is called a Water-Flood Project or Secondary Recovery

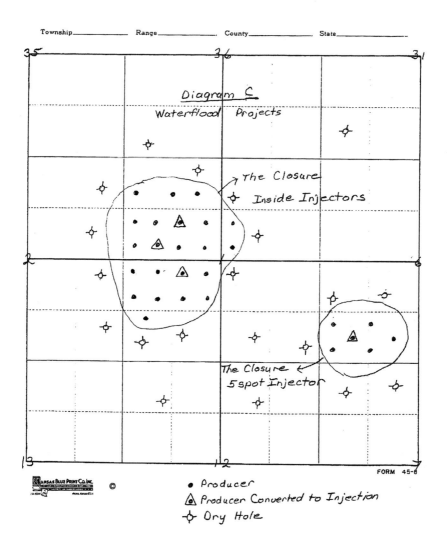

Diagram "D"
Disposal Well
Design

The Disposal Zone in this particular well is the open Hole. You can also have perforations. In Kansas, the Disposal zone has to be 50' below any oil bearing areas of the particular Reservoir. The Packer must be set within 50' of the Disposal Area. We also have shallow Disposal wells in the Cedar Hills Sands. They are all set up the same. The Annular Space above the Pkr. & between the inside of the Casing and outside of the Tubing, has to hold pressure. Some areas lower then others, but usually 300#. This is called a Mechanical Integrity Test (MIT). Makes sure you have no Casing or Tubing Leaks. It will be tested by the KCC every 5 years.

→ Casing

→ Tubing (Plastic Lined on Inside - Durolined or Seal-Tite)

→ Annulus (Area between Casing + outside of Tubing) must hold 300# in most areas.

→ Packer

{Open Hole (No Casing)

TD

166

14

FRACING

Every rock has a pressure where it will break or crack. This is called a frac gradient. Some rocks have high pressures and some have fairly low pressures.

Fracing consists of breaking a rock (zone) down, and pumping something into it. This something can be water, nitrogen, which expands over time, or sand, which serves as a propping agent. What you are trying to do with a frac is increase permeability. Remember, permeability is the ability of a liquid or gas, to flow through the rock to the well bore. We are trying to improve this through an artificial process.

Pressure is the key when dealing with a frac. You have to get to the frac gradient of the rock to do any good. We do this with volume. You can do these either through tubing or casing. Down tubing you become restricted with friction pressure. Tubing is much smaller than casing. Fracing down casing can drastically increase your volume and rates. In addition, the fracing companies have come up with chemicals that can drastically reduce friction pressure. For instance, I have done frac jobs, called slick water fracs, down 5 1/2" casing at 50 barrel per minute and the surface pressure only run 1,600# to 1,800#. This blows my mind. For instance, when pumping strictly water down 2 3/8" (2") tubing, you start to get some friction pressure at 2.5 to 3 barrel per minute. In other words, you can only shove so much down tubing before you actually become restricted and start building pressure because it will not take any more on its own.

Let me explain one thing about surface pressure. The pressure that you have on the surface is not the pressure you have at the bottom of the hole. You have hydrostatic pressure from the fluid itself. Hydrostatic pressure is the weight of the fluid from the surface to the bottom of the hole. In other words, depending on the type of fluid you have in the hole, be it salt water, freshwater, or oil, it weighs so much per foot. So let's say salt water weighs 400# per 1,000' of height from the bottom of the hole. If you have a well 4,000' deep, and the hole is full, you have 1,600# on the very bottom of the hole, just with the weight of the fluid itself. This is measured in pounds per square inch (PSI). Just so you get the idea, say that you have a 10' high tank with a diameter of 12'. You have a valve on the bottom of this tank and it is salt water, just as before. The tank is full to the 10' mark. If you put a gauge on the valve at the bottom of the tank, you would have 4# on the gauge. Volume means nothing. This is pounds per square inch. Height and weight of the fluid is what makes the pressure difference.

So, going back to the frac, when you have a 4,000' well and the hydrostatic pressure is #400 per 1,000' of fluid, and you have 1,600# pump pressure at the surface, the bottom hole actually has 3,200# on it. Now, as we are pumping this water down the hole, we are adding sand to it. We usually start out with say .25# of sand per gallon and we may get up to 2# or 3# of sand per gallon. We do this in stages. In other words, we pump so many gallons at the .25# sand and slowly build up to the larger amounts of sand. The water is carrying the sand to bottom. Sometimes we need a little thicker agent to carry the sand. We call this gel. It is a substance something like a thin Jell-O. It is a very good carrying agent. As you move up, pumping more sand per gallon, the surface pressure will actually go down because you have more weight per pound while going down the hole. Attached is diagram A, a procedure for fracing a well. Notice on the fracing schedule, you start out with a pad. From here you start with the sand and slowly increase the volume of sand on each stage. As you are doing the job, you need to keep track of when each stage hits the bottom. You have set a maximum pressure that you do not want to go over, before you started the job. You have done this because your casing or tubing is only good to a certain pressure. If you go over that pressure, you could easily blow a hole in the casing or tubing. Remember, we don't know everything that will happen when we are doing the job. Say you are pumping along, and as you are raising the rate of sand per gallon, suddenly the pressure jumps up to your maximum pressure. You are forced to shut down. When this happens, we call this screening out. In other words, the zone won't take anymore sand at your maximum pressure. Since you have shut down, all the sand in the casing will slowly drift to bottom and start piling up in the casing. Hopefully, you have gotten enough sand in the formation to do what you wanted. If you have tubing and a packer in the hole, you can let things settle down and release the packer and circulate the sand out of the hole, down past the perforations. You can then pull up above your zone and start swabbing the well down to see if your job did any good. All the time you have been swabbing the well down to see if you did any good, you should be checking to see if any of the sand is coming back. You will almost always get some sand back, but you need to watch and make sure you do not get the swab stuck in the hole.

Fracing is something you here about a lot in the news nowadays. Fracing has been going on for over 60 years. They were not as big back then, but they did the same thing and served the same purpose. Fracing is a safe process, as long as the well has been set up correctly. Kansas does things right when it comes to protecting freshwater. This was no always the case.

Let me explain why I say this. Most fracing is done down casing, or the production string, say 5 1/2" or 4 1/2" casing. Surface casing has been set to a certain point, say 225', to cover the freshwater in the upper section of the well. This 8 5/8" casing has been set and cemented from top to bottom on the outside of the casing. This would be protection number one. In addition, the production casing has been cemented on bottom and a DV tool or port collar has been run in the upper section of the well to cover the extreme salt water zones that lie right below the freshwater zones. This tool is usually set either in the anhydrite or right above it. This tool allows you to circulate cement around the outside of the production string, all the way up to surface. Thus, you have two layers of casing and two layers of cement protecting the freshwater zones.

We have people discussing fracing that have no idea what they are talking about. The only conclusion you can come too, is they need to know the subject matter or keep their mouth shut.

Diagram "A"

Frac Procedure

Trego County, KS, Sec.14-14S-21W
6 Tank Slickwater Frac
Marmaton Zone

Stage	Rate (bpm): 45 Volume (gals)	Prop Conc (ppg)	Fluid Type	Est. Pressure (psi): 2,600 Proppant Type & Mesh	Lbs Per Stage	Slurry BBLS	Cum. BBLS	Stage Time	Lbs per Minute
1	21,000		Slickwater	Pad		500.0	500.0	11.11	
2	7,000	0.10	Slickwater	30/50 Brown	700	167.4	667.4	3.72	188
3	7,000	0.20	Slickwater	30/50 Brown	1,400	168.2	835.6	3.74	375
4	7,000	0.30	Slickwater	30/50 Brown	2,100	168.9	1,004.6	3.75	559
5	9,000	0.40	Slickwater	30/50 Brown	3,600	218.2	1,222.8	4.85	742
6	9,000	0.50	Slickwater	30/50 Brown	4,500	219.2	1,441.9	4.87	924
7	9,000	0.60	Slickwater	30/50 Brown	5,400	220.1	1,662.1	4.89	1104
8	9,000	0.70	Slickwater	30/50 Brown	6,300	221.1	1,883.2	4.91	1282
9	9,000	0.80	Slickwater	30/50 Brown	7,200	222.1	2,105.3	4.94	1459
10	7,000	0.90	Slickwater	16/30 Brown	6,300	173.5	2,278.8	3.86	1634
11	6,000	1.00	Slickwater	16/30 Brown	6,000	149.4	2,428.2	3.32	1808
12	2,000	1.50	Slickwater	16/30 Resin Coated	3,000	50.9	2,479.1	1.13	#DIV/0!
13	1,500	2.00	Slickwater	16/30 Resin Coated	3,000	39.0	2,518.0	0.87	2654
Flush	3,900		Slickwater			92.9	2,610.9	2.05	
	1,500		Slickwater	Overflush		35.7	2,646.6	0.79	

105,900 Gals. Pumped
11,100 Gals. Tank Bottoms
120,000 Gals. Total Required

49,500 Lbs. Total Proppant Pumped
2,646.6 Bbls. Total Slurry Pumped
55.95 Minutes Total Time Elapsed

Percent Pad   20.29%

15

DIRECTIONAL DRILLING

Up until the last few years there had not been many directional wells drilled in the state of Kansas. Boy has that changed. We have companies coming out of the woodwork, trying this everywhere and in every zone. My personal opinion is that this has not been a very well thought out process. They are doing things and spending money on things that have not been tested.

Let me explain quickly, what a directional well really is. You are drilling a vertical hole to a certain point and then you gradually start to make a bend until you get to a point where you are drilling totally horizontal. Supposedly, if everything is done correctly, you know exactly what direction, and where you are going. I can tell you that this is not always the case. I have heard about directional wells that have ran into casing on conventional wells, so I know accuracy is not all that great. Attached is diagram A depicting a directional well.

These types of wells have been highly successful in the Balkan shale in North Dakota, Oklahoma in the Mississippian, and in Texas in many different zones. Let me try to explain why it has, and probably will be a failure in most of Kansas, other than the southern counties of Kansas in the Mississippian.

First of all, let's take a look at the Marmaton zone in western Kansas. This is a very low permeability zone. It has good bottom-hole pressure and will fill up fairly high when first treated. However, the drainage area is almost nothing, unless it has some water drive.

Secondly, the productive section of the Marmaton is usually only 6' to 16' thick. Try staying in this 6' to 16' section at 4,000' to 5,000' below the surface. It would be almost impossible. Estimated cost of these wells, when completed, will run somewhere around 2 to 2.5 million dollars. At $80 per barrel with a net revenue interest of say $64 per barrel, it will take 40,000 barrels just to pay these wells off. Unless I'm mistaken, most of these wells will never be profitable.

I just heard that one company tried this in the Lansing-Kansas City. I can't even imagine this! Try staying in zones 2' to 6' thick at 3,400'. Plus the fact that the top of this zone may move up or down 5' to 10' over 660'. This is just ridiculous. These companies have way too much money and are just throwing it away.

The Major oil companies moved out of Kansas about 30 years ago. A few of them, such as Shell Oil Company, have moved back in and have tried to take advantage of this new process. Before they moved in, acreage was going for about $10 to $30 per acre. These clowns moved in and started leasing acreage for $200 to $1,500 per acre. What do you think this has done to the little guy? It has shut the conventional projects down and made it impossible to pick up acreage.

I understand that Shell has learned their lesson and are moving out of Kansas again. They are in the process of writing off over a billion dollars in acreage expenses alone. Did these guys do their homework? I don't think so! These types of losses would put most companies out of business. All of the companies I know that are doing this, are publically funded companies. Some of these will go down. In other words, they will file bankruptcy.

I am not an expert, but I understand that these directional wells are drilled with motors that are run on the drill string. In other words, the motor is located in the bit itself. It can be controlled from the surface. This is much like boring a road crossing only you are much deeper. You have to make a gradual turn and then you can go horizontal. Many of these horizontal legs go out 1/4 to1/2 mile.

These directional wells have been highly successful in areas with thick pay zones, such as the Balkans, Texas, and Oklahoma. That's why I say that Kansas is one of the toughest areas in the world to operate. We operate with very thin zones with very limited permeability. Experience is very valuable in our area. Most of the areas I have worked in throughout Kansas will not be profitable when it comes to directional drilling. The zones are simply too small for this type of drilling to work. We do not have the expertise to drill horizontally in a 2' to 6' zone.

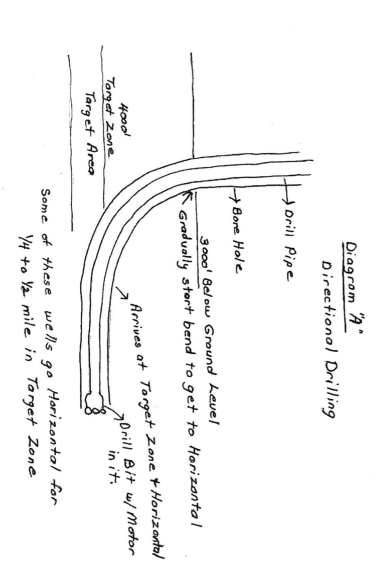

Diagram "A"
Directional Drilling

→ Drill Pipe

→ Bore Hole

3000' Below Ground Level

Gradually start bend to get to Horizontal

Arrives at Target Zone & Horizontal

Drill Bit w/ Motor in it.

4000'
Target Zone

Target Area

Some of these wells go Horizontal for ¼ to ½ mile in Target Zone

174

16

PLUGGING OF AN OIL OR GAS WELL

Every oil or gas well has a life. Just as in humans, these oil and gas wells come to an end. When a well comes to its economic limit—where it is no longer profitable and there is nothing left to do—the well must be plugged. Plugging entails cementing the well shut so it will never cause a problem.

First of all, back in chapter 4, we discussed the big decision. What if you drilled the well and you had nothing that was commercial, as far as oil or gas production? We would call this a dry hole. The drilling rig is still on location and you have just decided that it is a dry hole. How do you go about plugging the well?

You call the Kansas Corporation Commission office in your area. They will give you plugging orders. These orders entail spotting cement at certain points in the well bore. Depending on how deep and through what zones you have drilled, this will determine where these cement plugs will be spotted. Remember, your surface pipe was run early in this process and it was cemented from the top to the bottom on the outside of the casing. This will not be recovered. It will be left in the ground forever.

Now let's say you drilled through the Arbuckle, a water-driven zone. All the drill pipe will be run in the hole to the top of the Arbuckle formation. When pipe gets to this point, a 50 sack plug of cement will be spotted on bottom. The hole is full of mud. The cementer will figure out what it will take to get this plug right down on bottom. He will mix the 50 sacks and displace it right to the end of the pipe by pumping it down with drilling mud. Once this plug has been spotted, the rig crew will start coming out of the hole laying the drill pipe down in baskets. As you are coming out of the hole, you will stop at certain points and spot cement, as per orders of the KCC. Once you get to a certain point, up where freshwater and salt water meets, you circulate cement from this point to the surface. You do not want to ruin freshwater. Freshwater is becoming a real commodity.

Let me take a moment and explain what has happened over the years. You see, oil and gas drilling has been taking place over the last 100 years or so. Drilling of oil and gas wells was way ahead of any controlling agencies, such as the KCC. Plugging was not done in a manner to protect the freshwater. In other words, wells were not plugged properly. Much of our freshwater has been ruined by improperly plugged wells. Salt water has been allowed to commingle with freshwater. There is not much we can do to correct this travesty now. We need to ensure that we, as producers, never let this happen again.

Now for plugging of old producing wells, injection wells, and disposals. Your surface pipe is cemented from top to bottom on the outside of the casing when you drilled the well. In addition, you have a production string from the surface to the bottom of the hole that was drilled. This string does not have cement from the surface to the bottom of the hole. There are two possibilities on these wells.

The first possibility is that the bottom 500' to 1,000' of the casing has cement on the outside of the pipe. No other cementing has been done on the well. You definitely want to check out the records and make sure that no squeeze jobs have been done over the years in the upper sections. So, if you have a 3,500' well, there is no cement from the surface to about 2,500' to 3,000'. There are two ways to plug this well. You can back off or shoot off the casing from some point above the cement top on bottom. Once you have the casing free, you will

THE INNER WORKINGS OF THE OIL AND GAS BUSINESS

start out of the hole spotting cement plugs just like the drilling plug, except you are pulling casing. The KCC would tell you where they want the plugs. Once you get the casing out of the hole, it can be tested and reused if it is in good condition. The second option, if you chose to just leave the casing in the hole, is to perforate certain spots in the casing. The pipe will be left in the hole. If perforating is done, tubing needs to be run to bottom and the casing needs to be squeezed with cement. I personally do not believe this is the way to do this. Let me explain why. With only running tubing in the hole, you never know if any cement ever gets into the perforations that you put in the casing. The correct way to do this, in my opinion, would be to run a packer and separately squeeze cement into each one of these perforations. This is the only way to know that the well is plugged correctly. Why isn't this done? Simple, it costs money.

The second case is where the production string has been cemented on bottom as above, and then it was cemented on top from a certain point to the surface, on the outside of the casing. Often times the state will have us perforate what we call the salt section, which is below the anhydrite. This section is about 100' to 200' thick, which is made up of salt. In certain areas in Kansas, this salt is actually mined. You may have some of it on your kitchen table. From here, oftentimes, this well, depending on the integrity of the casing, the state will allow you to pump cement from the top of the casing, without running tubing. In my opinion, this is nuts! You are asking for trouble. Even if you do run tubing and fill the hole with cement, this is still a problem. How do you know you are getting cement into the perforations you put in the pipe at the salt section? You don't! Let me explain what has happened to several areas in Kansas due to the salt section.

On I-70, about two miles east of the Gorham, Kansas exit, a sinkhole has developed because of poorly plugged oil wells that were drilled back in the 60's and 70's. About 600' to 800' down, there is a salt water–bearing zone, called the Dakota, that is really corrosive. It is almost like an underground river. Below this, at about 3,000' to 3,200', we have the productive areas of the Lansing-Kansas City, which have been perforated and produced. These zones will take water on a vacuum. Lots of these old wells, over the years, have developed casing leaks in the Dakota. Thus, salt water has been running down into the old producing zones. During this time, a lot of these wells have developed casing leaks in the salt section, which is between the Dakota and the Lansing-Kansas City producing zones. Thus water was flowing from the Dakota, into the salt section, and on down to the producing zones. This flow eats out the salt in the salt section. In other words, the liquid flowing through the salt section dissolves and eats away the salt section. Anytime you have a liquid with movement flowing through this section, you have a good chance of eating away the salt. Over the many years that this happens, you develop a void in the salt section. This is like a cavern. The overburden of the earth, the weight of the earth above the salt, begins to sink on the surface. Over time, this will all of the sudden collapse at the surface. In other words, this is a disaster waiting to happen. One day this sinkhole will fall out of sight. The state of Kansas has tried to fix this several times, but it's way too late. This is not like a balloon. You can't fill it up and hope that it will stay. Attached, is a diagram A explaining what has happened.

How can we avoid these mistakes? You have to plug above and below the salt section so that fluid will not move through this section. Without fluid movement through this section, this will not happen. Perforating the salt section is not the answer. Like I said before, if we don't know for sure whether we're getting cement into the salt section, this is not a fix since you are still pumping a liquid into it. Oftentimes, when leaks develop in the salt section on a producing well, it is tough to get a squeeze job to hold. The reason for this is the fact that you are trying to pump a liquid into the salt section. Remember, all of this can happen on the outside of the pipe if you don't have a good cement job.

Plugging of wells is very important. Freshwater is becoming really hard to find. These poorly plugged wells have ruined a lot of freshwater. This is the final act in the life of an oil or gas well.

Diagram "A"

- Sink Holes -

Sink Holes are formed by fluid movement. A well develops a leak from the upper section called the Dakota. Over time, this corrosive water will develop a leak in the Salt Section. The salt section is exactly what it sounds like, a complete zone of salt. Once you have a hole in the salt Section, this water movement will desolve the salt and make a cavern. Over time the over burden of the earth will become so heavy it will sink. Thus, you have a sink Hole.

Surface Casing - Cemented from Bottom to surface

→ Long String - 4½" or 5½"

→ Dakota Formation (Water Bearing Zone - much Like an underground River - Salt Water)

Hole in Casing

Hole in casing

→ Salt Section

Water comes in from the Dakota & passes through the salt - Eroding the salt away and then moves down into the old producing formations

Perfs

Producing Zones

17

Safety

This business is a business where safety is a must. There are lots of different things that can happen in this business, and most of them are not good. I personally do very little physical labor. My job is more mental. However, most of the jobs in the oil business are not that fortunate. Let me explain some of the things that can happen.

First of all, the drilling rigs. These men on drilling rigs are in very precarious positions on a daily basis. In other words, they can get hurt quite easily. They are dealing with heavy equipment such as drill pipe and tongs. This drill pipe is flying around all the time. Every time you pick up a joint of drill pipe, anything can happen. The joint could drop or be put on your foot. These joints weigh hundreds of pounds. Safety shoes, such as steel-toed shoes are a must, but these can't save you when a joint lands on your shoe. Also, hard hats are a must. Things can fall out of the derrick. Even the most tiny and light thing, such as a small bolt coming loose and falling out of the derrick, can be very dangerous. I had the unfortunate luck of this happening to me several years ago on a drilling rig. Luckily, it just stung a little. It definitely got my attention. Things that are used on the rig such as slips, elevators, and tongs are all very heavy. Thus, your back can easily get overloaded. You need to use your head. These drilling rigs have what we call catlines, which run off the draw works of the rig, to pick up really heavy things. They should definitely be used when they can be. You need to always be aware of danger.

Many of these same problems can be encountered on the work-over rigs. Here you are dealing with tubing and rods. This equipment is not quite as heavy, but there are still lots of ways to get hurt. Fingers, hands, and toes can easily be in the way. Tongs are a great problem. It is easy to get your fingers in the tongs and have them cut off. It's easy to get things smashed. You need to always be aware of your surroundings. One time while we were swabbing a well back after treating with acid, we were swabbing into a pit. The well had been treated several times, and we had never seen an acid kick. However, after about three pulls with the swab, the hose started to move. There were several of us sitting around the pit, watching the swabs. All of the sudden you could see the hose start to move. I yelled at the guys that we needed to get out of the way. About five of us started running. The owner of the well was right behind me. We did not have the swab hose tied down. The hose started flying around from the acid kick. The hose was four inch rubber with a four-inch hammer union on the end of it. It hit the owner in the head and knocked him out of his shoes. Luckily, he was not hurt badly, but it was a good lesson. Always tie down your swab lines. The best policy is to be oversafe. If you think something could happen, prepare for it.

As for chemicals, the same is true. These are very strong products that can be highly detrimental to the skin or eyes. Always wear protective gear such as gloves or glasses when dealing with these materials. Acid can eat the skin. Protective clothing is also essential. Many of these chemicals when combined can become combustible.

Almost every job in this business is dangerous, from pipe testers to water haulers. The EPA and OSHA have safety regulations that are usually quite good. Once in a while they get out of line, mainly because they have never really experienced the business. One example of this is the fire-retardant uniforms that have to be worn in our area. First of all, there are not many places in this area where fire is a real possibility. Many times in the summer, the heat gets up to more than a hundred degrees. In this uniform, more health problems are caused by heat exhaustion than will ever be caused by fires. Common sense would be a more prudent answer to our problems. I personally don't believe the government needs to tell us exactly what we need to do. First of all, most of them have never been here. It's tough to pass rules and regulations when you have never done a certain job. In other words, they need to stay out of our business.

No matter how safe you try to be, things will always happen. With all of these things, you need to use common sense. Accidents happen and will happen. We cannot protect everyone. Just use your head and do the best you can for your own safety.

CONCLUSION

This book has come full circle, from putting a new prospect together to the plugging of oil and gas wells. This should give you a good idea of what is involved in the oil and gas business.

To become efficient in this business you must get experience. You can learn things in school that will help you, but to become efficient, you must gain experience.

There are many, many jobs in this business. If you are interested in getting into this business, you need to start at the bottom and slowly move up. You can learn something new almost every day. Specialization has become a large part of this business. There are many specialized jobs, such as logging engineers, chemical men, cementers, acidizers, and so on. When I got into this business, things were much less complicated. Nowadays, it's tough to become familiar with everything. This all takes time and lots of experience.

Kansas is what we in the business call shallow-hole country. We produce oil from 300' to around 4,500' in the areas I work. Most of these principles would apply to deep-hole country. Some of these wells run 10,000' to 15,000' deep. Things such as drilling rigs, workover rigs, and casing run in larger sizes. Many of these deeper hole wells have 3 to 4 strings of casing. They start out with 13 7/8" casing, all the way down to 4 1/2" casing.

One of the most important things to learn in this business is the language. You see, dope comes in 5-gallon buckets, and joints are 30' to 45' long. That's just a little oil field joke. The dope is thread dope, and the joints are tubing and casing. To help you out with this, I have included a glossary at the end of this book. Hopefully this will make it a little easier to understand. I hope you enjoyed the trip.

GLOSSARY

3-D imaging—A seismic interpretation of what each horizon looks like using sound waves and time to determine depths.

a barrel of oil—A barrel of oil equals 42 gallons.

accelerator—Calcium chloride is a chemical that can be added to cement to heat it up and accelerate the setup time for cement.

acid plug job—You pump acid and rock salt in stages. For example, you start out with 500 gallons of acid. You then follow with 250# to 500# of rock salt, which in theory will plug off the zone that the acid just went into. Right behind the plug, you would follow up with more acid and hopefully break down another zone. You should see the pump pressure come up when the plug hits and drop off when the acid gets on bottom to break down another zone. You can do this several times, depending on the number of zones you are treating. Whatever the number is, you would run one less plugs.

anchor—Pipe below packers on a DST.

anhydrite—This is a hard stringer of rock in the upper part of the hole in Kansas that is an excellent marker when drilling a well.

annulus—This is the area between the tubing and the casing.

authority for expenditure (AFE)—A rough estimate of costs to do a job.

basket—These are run on the outside of the casing to keep hydrostatic pressure off a low pressure zone. Also, these are used in the anhydrite so cement does not fall when trying to circulate cement on the upper stage cement job.

blow back—When the tool is closed from the initial flow, the line to the bubble bucket is blown down. While the tool is shut in, the line is put back in to the bubble bucket to see if there is any blow. If there is, this usually indicates gas. This blow is called blow back.

blowout preventer (BOP)—This is a tool that is installed on your surface pipe after it has been set. The tool's primary objective is to shut off blowouts. This is your last line of defense when a well blows out and gets out of control.

bonded—Pipe has cement around it.

bottom hold-down insert pump—This is a type of pump that has the hold-down on the bottom of the pump. The seating cups are on the bottom of the pump and seat into the seating nipple.

breakdown job—This is the first treatment with acid on a zone.

bridge plug—Tool run in casing on tubing to isolate the bottom of the hole or any perforations from below the zone you are working on. You can come off the bridge plug and leave it in the hole, allowing nothing to go by from the bottom or the top.

bubble bucket—When the DST tool is on bottom and the tool has been opened, a five-gallon bucket of water is placed on the drilling floor with a hose from the top of the drill pipe into the bucket. The bucket will start bubbling when the tool is opened and will build to the bottom of the bucket as fluid comes into the drill pipe during the DST openings.

caliper log—Tells you the hole size at any given point.

canning a gun barrel—You climb to the top of the gun barrel and open the hatch. You then tie a can on the bottom of the gauge line and lower it into the oil and let the can fill up with oil. You then lower the can until it floats. Measure the distance from the oil on gauge line to the bottom of the can. This tells you how much oil is on top of the water in the gun barrel.

cased hole log—This is a log that will be run after casing has been set and the cement has had time to set up. This log is called a correlation/bond log. It has a gamma ray log on the left-hand side of the log that has been tied into the open hole logs. The cement bonding portion of the log is on the right-hand side of the log along with the collars on the casing.

casing leak—This is a hole in the casing that is not where it should be. Over time, the casing has developed a hole. Oftentimes this leads to lots of water, depending on where the leak is.

catlines—Ropes that can be run off the draw works of a drilling rig to pick up heavy equipment.

centralizers—These are installed on casing (outside of) to center pipe in the well bore.

choke—This controls the volume of gas sent out of the separator (pack unit) to the meter run. This controls the volume of gas to be sold.

closure—A zone that has limits and is isolated.

commingling of zones—Several different zones producing in the same well.

communicated holes—Holes you can set a packer in between and fluid goes out the casing and up the backside to the next set of holes.

conditioning the hole—Circulate till hole is clean.

coning—Sucking water to the well bore by pumping the fluid down to fast. In other words, you start the well producing too much fluid and lower the fluid level so fast that the water begins coming in so quickly that the fluid level will jump back up.

contouring—Drawing by using subsea footages.

contract pumper—A contract pumper pays all the expenses, pick up, fuel, insurance, etc. They are paid so much a month per stop. A stop is a well or tank battery. Say they get $100 per stop. Thus, for a one well lease, they would be paid $200, $100 for the well and $100 for the tank battery. This would amount to $200 per month for the lease.

cross section—You have drawn a line across a 3-D project. The cross section is composed of the wave lengths across this project on this line.

Dakota zone—This is a water-bearing zone, both freshwater and salt water, in areas is like an underground river. Mainly you find this in Kansas.

dehydration of cement—Squeezing water out of the cement so it gets hard.

density porosity log—Determines the rock bulk density along the well bore.

doc squeeze—This is a cement squeeze where diesel fuel is mixed into the cement instead of water. The theory is that the cement will only set up in the water and let the oil come through.

double drum pulling unit—This type of unit has two drums. One drum is to pull tubing and rods, and the second drum is a sand line that has a line that will reach the bottom of the hole.

drilling break—When a zone drills faster than it normally would.

drilling nipple—This is a piece of surface casing that fits on top of the surface casing that comes to the surface under the drilling floor so that the samples will make it to surface.

drill stem test (DST)—A test taken on a drilling well to test a specific area or zone in an uncased well.

drilling table—A rotating table on the drilling floor of the rig in which the kelly bushing fits to rotate the kelly, drill pipe, and bit.

drilling under surface—This is when you start drilling after you have let surface pipe set up from the cement job.

dry hole—A well that has been drilled to total depth and has no productive value.

dump floods—Dumping water down a well in hopes of increasing production. Usually when you develop a waterflood, you have a plan. With a dump flood you are simply hoping.

DV tool or port collars—These are used to cement a specific area of the pipe above your primary cement job on the bottom of the hole. DV tools are run when you want to do the staged job when the well is drilled and casing is set. A port collar is done when you want to do the staged job before or after completing the well. You run an opening tool on tubing to do a port collar.

economic limit—The point where the cost of producing oil is more than the oil that can be produced. The value of the well is unprofitable.

final flow—The DST tool is rotated and open to flow for a second time. This will usually be about the same length of time as the initial flow or just a little longer, depending on the blow.

final flow pressure (FFP)—Starting and ending pressures on the second flow of a DST.

final shut-in—After the final flow period, the DST tool will be closed again for a certain length of time. This period is at least as long as the first shut-in and sometimes twice as long. You want to get the bottom-hole pressure curve to roll over.

final shut-in pressure (FSIP)—on a DST, this would be the highest pressure reading on the second shut-in.

flow T—This goes on top of the tubing above the ground. It is T shaped with 1" on one side and 2" or 3" on the other side. The 2" or 3" goes to the lead line. The 1" is called the bleeder.

frac pressure—This is a pressure at which you can force a substance into a rock. Every rock has a frac pressure. These are all different.

free ride to bottom of the hole—Operator pays no bills or anything until the decision to set pipe has been made. Expenses are paid from the point of pipe setting only. From this point expenses are paid for their share on.

gamma ray log—This log measures radioactivity to determine what type of rocks are present in the well bore.

gas-driven reservoir—Gas is the primary force driving the oil to the well bore.

gas measurements—gas is measured in 1,000 cubic feet volumes. Say you have 5,000 cubic feet of gas. This would be 5 MCFs. Gas is sold in MCFs.

gas pack unit—This is the controlling device for getting your gas to the pipeline.

ground level elevation—This is the elevation relative to sea level.

gun barrel—The largest vessel at the tank battery. This is the vessel where water, gas, and oil are separated.

hand-treating—Pumping chemical down the annulus and circulating the hole for a few hours and then coming back and putting the well back on production.

highs—Structurally speaking relative to other wells in the area.

hydrostatic pressure—This is the pressure due to height, not volume.

independent geologist—A geologist who works on his own with no particular company.

initial flow of a DST (IF)—When the DST tool is on bottom, the tool is opened hydraulically. This period, from the time the tool is opened until it is shut in, is called the initial flow.

initial flow pressure (IFP)—Starting and ending pressure readings on first opening on a DST.

initial shut-in (ISI)—On a DST, after the tool has been opened for the first time, it will then be shut-in to get a bottom hole pressure reading.

initial shut-in pressure (ISIP)—This would be the highest pressure reading on the first shut-in. Usually this would be at the end of the shut-in period.

injection well—Wells that take water in a waterflood.

injection rate—Pumping in a liquid at so many barrels per minute (bpm) at a certain pressure.

INS acid—Intensified nonswelling acid. This acid helps to keep clays and shale from swelling.

insert pump—A pump that is inserted into the inside of the tubing on rods.

instant shut-in pressure—This is the pressure that is on the well head at the end of pumping into a zone.

investors—People who are willing to take the chance with their own money to drill a new well.

kelly—A square piece of pipe 6" × 6" and 50' long used to drill each joint as we go down the hole.

kelly bushing—A bushing on the kelly about 1' × 1' that is attached to the kelly and slides up and down on the kelly.

kelly bushing measurement—Everything will be measured from this point on the well. This is the ground level elevation plus the substructure footage to top of the rotary table.

lag time—The amount of time that it takes for samples to get from the bottom of the hole to the surface.

landing joint—This is a partial joint on top of the casing to spot the top of the casing. For surface casing this will be spotted about 2' below ground level. For production casing this will be about 6" above ground level.

landman—A professional who leases land.

limited entry—This is a method of treating 2 or 3 zones at a time with 1 hole each in each zone. The holes are at 3/8". The theory is that you can get 2.5 bpm into each hole. Thus, if you get to 7.5 bpm, you have gotten into all three of the zones. If only two holes, all you would need is 5 bpm.

load—This is the total amount of fluid that has been pumped into a zone. This includes the acid, flush, and tubing and casing volume.

long stroke—The double drum unit makes the pump go up and down. You can feel a blow on the tubing. You are pumping or lifting the fluid inside the tubing.

lubricator—This is a partial joint of casing with hammer unions on both ends and a 2" valve coming off the casing as a blow down.

A pack off is on top to stop fluid or gas from coming out the top. The pack off can be hydraulically pressured up.

mechanical integrity test (MIT)—The annulus between the casing and the tubing is tested by using pressure, and it must hold for a certain amount of time. This ensures the casing has no leaks. In Kansas, this pressure is 300# and must hold for 30 minutes. It is done every 5 years to make sure the casing still has integrity. This is done on every disposal well or injection well, but not on producers.

micro log—Permeability log.

minipacks—Controlling devices in which gas runs through a heating process to a choke on the end of the vessel. The gas flows through a water bath that is heated. This will heat the gas.

misrun—When the DST tool is set, if fluid does not stay at the surface on the outside of the hole or the drill pipe, then you have a misrun.

mousehole—A hole in the ground that has been drilled to hold the next joint of drill pipe to be added to the drill string.

mud anchor—A partial joint of tubing, say 15' long with perforations in the top 3' with the rest of the joint being solid and orange peeled on the bottom. The slots or perforations are for fluid to come into the pump and tubing. Trash will fall to the bottom of the mud anchor.

mud up—This is when you switch from water to mud when drilling a well. You displace the water out of the hole and replace it with drilling mud.

NE acid—This is nonemulsified acid.

net revenue interest—This is the revenue interest after the royalty and overriding royalties have been subtracted from the total revenues.

neutron porosity log—This log assumes the reservoir pore spaces are filled with either water or oil and then measuring the amount of hydrogen atoms (neutrons) in the pores.

oil in place—This is a scientific calculation of the volume in barrels of the oil in a formation. This is just a good educated guess.

open acreage—Acreage not under lease.

open hole—When pipe is set off bottom, the well will be completed open hole, if the bottom of the hole is the target zone. The bottom of the hole will not be cased. This is called open hole. The distance from the rotary total depth (RTD) to where the casing is set is called the open hole.

overflush—The volume of water you push into a formation once all the acid has been put into the zone.

open hole logs—Logs ran before casing is set on a well.

overriding royalty interest (ORRI)—An interest added on for putting the project together. Just like a royalty interest, it does not pay expenses.

packer—A tool used to isolate a zone or area from the top. Slips on the packer, will push the

rubbers out against the casing or walls of the pipe. These can either be tension-type packers or set-down-type packers. They are set by turning the packer right or left, depending on what type of packer you are working with.

parted rods—A down-hole rod that has broken.

parted tubing—Tubing that has separated downhole.

pattern of injection—Depending on the size of the field, you can locate injectors on the outside, inside, or as a five-spot.

permanent plug—This is a cast iron bridge plug (CIBP) that is set on a wireline.

permeability—The ability of a liquid to flow through a rock to the well bore.

pipe testers—This is a crew of two people with a high-pressure truck who tests every joint on a rack to 6,000#, looking for holes, blowouts, bad threads, and bad collars.

plug back total depth—Once pipe has been set on the well, the bottom of the hole will be where the plug stopped, which should be the latch down on top of the shoe joint. Also, plug back total depth could be a cast iron bridge plug that has been set or cement that has not been drilled out after a squeeze job.

plugging an oil or gas well—This entails cementing the well shut.

polymer—A gelled substance that works as a net for holding water back yet lets oil through to the well bore. The polymer is pumped back into the formation and given a little time to set up before it is put back on production.

pony rods—Rods come in 25' long lengths. Pony rods are from 2' to 10' in length. They are used to space the pump in the right position.

porosity—This is the ability of a rock to hold hydro-carbons or liquids.

primary production—Production produced from day one until a well is included in a secondary recovery project such as a waterflood.

promoters—Usually these people are shady people who try to pull the wool over investors. They have given the oil business a bad name.

pulling units—Units that pull and run tubing and rods in oil or gas wells.

pumped off or pounding—When the rods are on the down stroke, the ball and seat on the bottom of the pump will allow fluid to come into the barrel of the pump. If the pump barrel fills all the way, you will see nothing. If the barrel only partially fills, you can see the rods jump; or wiggle. Sometimes you have to grab the polish rod and literally feel it jump. This is called the pound. The well is pumped off. The pump is pumping all the fluid that the well will produce.

rathole—A hole that is drilled at the beginning of the process where the kelly will go when not in use.

resistivity log (dual induction log)—Measures electric resistivity.

rock salt job—This is for communicated zones. Pump acid and rock salt in stages as plugging agent to break down each zone. The rock salt plugs off the first zone that is broken down so that the acid on the next stage breaks down the next zone.

rotor—This is the chrome piece that looks like a corkscrew. It will be run on the rods of a screw pump and goes into the stator. As the rods rotate, the fluid is moved up the tubing with the rotor inside the stator.

roustabout—These are common laborers who make surface equipment repairs or things to get wells on production such as lay lead lines, change out gun barrels and stock tanks. Mainly they repair equipment that is above ground.

royalty interest (RI)—This is the mineral owners share of a producing well. In Kansas this is usually 12.5% with no expenses, 12.5% of everything produced off the acreage. The mineral owner is not always the landowner. Oftentimes the minerals have been sold separately from the land.

salt water disposal well—A well in which produced salt water is put back into the ground. That is how we get rid of our salt water. This will be put into a zone that is nonproductive.

scratchers—These are installed on the outside of the casing to scratch the mud off the walls of zones so you can get a good cement job.

screening out—When you hit your maximum pressure on a frac job and you have to shut down.

directional drilling—This is a well that starts out drilling a vertical hole to a certain point and then gradually makes a bend until they are drilling a totally horizontal hole.

seating nipple—This is run on the bottom part of your tubing. It is 1.1' long. It is beveled on both ends and is smaller in diameter than your tubing. You can run it either way. The pump cannot go through the seating nipple. This is where the seating cups on an insert pump seat. When it wears out on one end, you can just turn it over and run it back in the hole using the other end. Also, with a swab bar, while you are swabbing on a well, you should always run a seating nipple on the bottom of your tubing. The bottom of your swab bar will have a no-go on it that will not go through the seating nipple. This is important because if something happens to your sand line, the swab will not go past the seating nipple. It can be fished by pulling the tubing.

secondary recovery oil—Oil that is produced because of waterflooding.

shoe joint—This is usually the first joint of casing run in the well when you are casing a new well. The guide shoe goes on the threaded end of the pipe (very bottom of the well). A latch-down or float assembly goes in the collar of the shoe joint. This joint will have cement in it after the pipe has been set.

short trip—On a well being drilled, you have drilled a lot of hole and never really reamed the hole clean. You pull the bit up the hole. Oftentimes it will pull tight. Usually you pull it up at least halfway to knock the walls clean. You then run back to bottom and condition the hole to get what you have knocked off the walls out of the hole.

single drum pulling unit—This type of unit has only one drum, a tubing drum, to pull tubing and rods. It does not have a sand line.

sluff—Cuttings from side of the hole that are from different areas than where the bit is drilling.

spontaneous potential log—Characterizes rock formation properties.

spudding—This is when you begin drilling hole for the well.

squeeze job—Pumping cement into a hole or set of holes to shut them off. This is like a patch.

stagging—Pumping up to a certain pressure and shutting down for a time, on and off.

standoff—On the perforating gun, this is the length between the center of the collar locator and the first shot on the gun.

stator—This is like a barrel on a tubing pump. It goes on the bottom of the tubing in a screw pump. It is made of very hard rubber. The rotor will go into the stator.

straddle test—This is a DST with a packer on bottom and top to isolate a specific area of the well bore. It will have tailpipe below the bottom packer clear to TD. These would be run after looking at a log and deciding that you may have missed something.

strapping the pipe—Measuring it on the way out of the hole.

DST tool—This is a set of two packers with a certain amount of tailpipe with holes in some of the tailpipe, to test a certain area of a well being drilled. It will have two sets of recorders that record flow pressures and BHP's.

Suite of logs—A grouping of different kinds of open hole logs.

sure shot—This device is dropped down the drill pipe right before you come out of the hole, and it will tell you how straight the hole is that you are drilling.

swabbing—Pulling fluid out of the hole, either through tubing or casing with rubber cups on a stem and sand line.

swab down—Once you have done something to a zone, whether it be acid treatment, frac, and the like, we may let the well set for a few minutes or overnight. We then begin swabbing this fluid back. We call this the swab down. We keep track of how much fluid we get back on the swab down. If possible, we try to swab it down to the bottom of the hole. If this can be done, we usually make two pulls off bottom and call this the swab down. If we can't, we swab it down until we think we have the load back. Once we have the swab down, we can put the well on test.

top hold-down insert pump—This is a type of pump that has the hold-down on the top of the pump. The seating cups are on the top of the pump and seat into the seating nipple.

total depth (TD)—This will be the bottom of the drilled well.

traveling barrel pump—On most insert pumps the plunger is the moving part. On the traveling barrel pump, the barrel is what goes up and down.

truck-treating—Special trucks that pump chemical and flush with lease water down the annulus of the well on a regular basis.

tubing conveyed gun—This type of perforating gun is run on the bottom of your tubing. A logging truck spots the gun exactly where you want to shoot it once the tubing has been run in the hole. An orbit valve is placed on the tubing, and the annulus is closed in. Once this has been done, a rod is dropped down the tubing, and the gun is detonated.

vacuum—A well that takes water on its own is said to be taking the water on a vacuum.

wall cake—When caliper log is on the left-hand side of the 7 7/8" borehole line. This is the first indicator of permeability.

wash out—When the caliper log is on the right-hand side of the 7 7/8" borehole line.

water-driven reservoir—Water is the primary driving force of oil to the well bore.

waterflooding—This is usually done in a gas driven reservoir. It is a process of injecting water into a well and zone to move the oil to other producers, thus replacing gas with water as the primary mover.

wet tubing—Say you're standing valve would not come out with the plunger. You must end up pulling the tubing to get the standing valve out of the hole. The tubing will be full of fluid. As you break out each joint, you will get water and oil that is in that joint. Thus the tubing is wet.

wildcat—A well that is more than half a mile from any other well ever drilled.

working interest (WI)—Percentage of the project a person purchases. This is also the percentage of expenses that the person will pay expenses on this project.

workovers—When you have to go back in on a well to repair leaks, retreat zones, open new zones, and so on.

ABOUT THE AUTHOR

Terry W. Piesker was born in Lyons, Kansas. He presently resides in Victoria, Kansas, about 10 miles east of Hays.

Terry is presently an Independent Oil and Gas Consultant with 40 years of experience working for large and small Oil Companies. During his career he has spent 1 year in the Rockies and 1 year in the Mountains of East Tennessee, but most of his time has been in Kansas on the Central Kansas Uplift. He has a son and two Step-sons. Both of his Step-sons are in the Oil Business.

About two years ago, his youngest Step-son moved back from Kansas City to Russell, Kansas to help his dad with his Independent Oil Company. Knowing nothing about the business, his wife asked him, "Is there a book he could get to learn the oil business." He jokingly laughed, "The only way to learn this business is through experience." This got him thinking about the basics of the business that could at least get him started. He started by giving him a few Chapters at a time. This way he would have some idea how the business works and what it entails. Over the next two years, the book developed. He got to thinking, this might make an excellent book for anyone interested in the business, from rig hands, to Petroleum Engineers, to Investors who want to know how their money is being spent.

Terry and his wife enjoy traveling and playing golf, along with spending time with their children and ten grandchildren.

CPSIA information can be obtained at www.ICGtesting.com
Printed in the USA
LVOW12s1927010115

421113LV00001B/39/P

9 781634 172240